D1156341

THE ITALIAN DRAWINGS
AT WINDSOR CASTLE

GENERAL EDITOR :
A. F. BLUNT

CANALETTO DRAWINGS

BY K. T. PARKER

PHAIDON

VENICE: THE CAMPANILE DAMAGED BY LIGHTNING, 1745

(Cat. No. 55)

THE DRAWINGS
OF
ANTONIO CANALETTO
IN THE COLLECTION OF
HIS MAJESTY THE KING
AT WINDSOR CASTLE

BY

K. T. PARKER

OXFORD & LONDON

THE PHAIDON PRESS LTD

1 Cromwell Place, London, S.W.7
Distributed in the U.S.A. by the Oxford University Press
114 Fifth Avenue, New York
and issued in all other countries by
George Allen and Unwin Ltd.
40 Museum Street, London, W.C.1

1948
MADE IN GREAT BRITAIN
PRINTED AT THE BAYNARD PRESS · LONDON
BOUND BY KEY & WHITING LTD · LONDON

FOREWORD

IT MAY BE WELL to explain briefly the principle on which the 143 items of this Catalogue have been arranged. This would hardly be necessary had a purely chronological principle been followed—had it been practicable to adopt a method so obvious, so straightforward, and in general so satisfactory. But, for divers reasons, such an arrangement could not well be carried out for the Canaletto series which concerns us here : for one, because the artist seems to have worked simultaneously in different styles, the one of more pronounced mannerism, the other of less, according to the type of drawing he was engaged upon ; furthermore, because the bulk of the Windsor Collection seems to be so concentrated on the 1730's and early '40's (without a preciser dating being indicated) that no real clarity could be achieved without further subdivision. The fact is, moreover, that the interest of date, however important it may be, is with Canaletto almost invariably coupled with an interest of place—this to a considerably greater degree than is the case with other artists of his own class. It seemed desirable, therefore, from the very start to combine, as far as possible, some sort of logic of topography with a logic of time ; and so a sequence of views of Venice, the surrounding islands, Padua, the Terra-ferma, Rome and London resulted, within each of which sections the factor of chronology was taken into account. But obviously there are Venetian views which are later than the Paduan and Roman, later indeed than the London views, and yet must precede them in the adopted arrangement. Obviously, too, by striving to attain some sort of ordered topographical sequence within each section, a straightforward chronological sequence (so far as it might be ascertainable) had on occasion to be interrupted. It is certainly not claimed that the result here achieved is in every way satisfying. It is hoped, however, that the reader will be aware as he passes from one item to the next that the arrangement is not a casual one, but the result of a good deal of reflection and experiment, and an endeavour to reconcile to some extent the various possible lines of approach.

For reasons which the Introduction will later explain, the problem of whether a drawing really is or is not the work of the Master's hand comes in for less discussion than in most catalogues of this kind. It remains to be seen whether the argument that, because a drawing came from Consul Smith's Collection, it was surely from the hand of Canaletto himself, not that of an assistant, will carry conviction in the long run. Nothing would be easier than to reject dogmatically everything that is less good than the best. It would be much harder to convince oneself that Canaletto was really a Master who imposed such an exacting standard on his output, whether as a painter or draughtsman. The paintings from miscellaneous collections that are referred to in the critical notes are, though numerous, by no means all that might have claimed our attention, had it not seemed likely that, by adducing more, the issue would be complicated rather than clarified. Nor does the mention of any picture necessarily imply that its genuineness, its execution by Canaletto himself, is vouched for. Sometimes the type, rather than the hand, is what seemed of interest. Moreover the pictures, despite their numbers at Windsor, are often widely dispersed and difficult to keep track of. They come and go. Photographs do not tell all.

Again, nothing conclusive is claimed for what is said in these pages about the personality of Consul Smith. It was pitched, not unintentionally, in a minor key; but evidence may yet be discovered which will throw a different light on the character of this interesting man.

I am sincerely grateful to Mr. E. K. Waterhouse for the generous and unprompted loan of a most useful collection of working material; to sig. Fabio Mauroner for much local information concerning his own and Canaletto's native city; and to Mr. J. Byam Shaw for his time and trouble in mitigating some of the many shortcomings of the draft of my Introduction. I am further indebted to Professor L. B. Namier for some essential references concerning George III; to Miss Sylvia Groves for information about pens, and Mr. A. Van Der Put about heraldry; to Mr. A. E. Popham, Mr. Francis Watson, and Mr. Francis Wormald for help or information of one kind or another; to Mr. I. G. Robertson and Mr. John Woodward both for constructive aid and unselfish 'fagging'; to Miss Helen Gibson for drawing the map; and to the Witt Library for the loan of various photographs. Finally, it is a pleasure and duty combined to thank Sir Owen Morshead, the Royal Librarian, and his assistant, Miss A. H. Scott Elliot; Professor Anthony Blunt, the editor of the series; and Mr. L. Goldscheider, the ever resourceful and obliging representative of the Phaidon Press.

K. T. P.

Detail from Plate 64

TABLE OF CONTENTS

The numbers in the margins of the Introduction
refer to the Drawings
as listed in the Catalogue, *not* to the Plates.

INTRODUCTION

The extraordinary abundance with which Canaletto's work is represented at Windsor is one of the most remarkable features of the Royal Collection. Even by the very exceptional standards obtaining in the Castle Library—where it is really nothing out of the common to find drawings by a single artist amounting to a substantial proportion of his whole known output—even by Windsor standards the Canaletto series is outstanding. It is not merely an accumulation, such as is frankly the case with certain other Italian artists; it combines variety and balance with the weight of numbers. If the collection were confined to drawings alone, its importance would still be of a very high order; but including, as it does, series equally remarkable of the artist's work as an etcher and painter, there is none to rival it. Here, within the compass of a single collection, the whole range of Canaletto's production, the full measure of his genius, are revealed.

It is obvious that such a concentration of material could only come about as the result of special circumstances; and it will be well to start by describing these circumstances in some detail, familiar though they may be already in general outline. The reader will hardly need to be reminded that the Windsor Canaletto collection as we know it to-day was (with the exception of two pictures) purchased entire by George III. What is far more significant, however, is that the vendor, the original maker of the collection, was a man who lived in close and constant touch with the artist, and acquired it from him, piece by piece. It is perhaps common knowledge that Joseph Smith and Canaletto were long and intimately associated. But just as the details of the transaction, by which the collection became the property of the Crown, have been very inaccurately and inconsistently recorded, so also has the relationship between the two men given rise to frequent misunderstanding.

Of the many writers who have referred to their connexion, practically no two have represented it in quite the same light, and it will be observed that they are often completely at variance. At first mere shades of difference in the interpretation of Smith may become noticeable: to one he is the friend and admirer of the artist, to another, the generous and benevolent patron. But in other accounts a very different conception appears: such terms as 'business manager', 'agent', or 'virtual director' of the artist's output, strike a new note altogether; the suggestion of a commercial relationship is introduced, and in some versions, even, there is the assumption of a recognized business partnership. Finally, at the opposite end of the scale, we find the noble benefactor of the first picture transformed into nothing better than the unscrupulous retailer of an underpaid artist.

The truth seems to lie somewhere midway between the two extremes. There is certainly no reason to believe that the two men ever fell out; the fact that Smith is known to have solicited certain letters of introduction on the artist's behalf disposes of the assertion that Canaletto's journey to England was a pretext for escaping from an irksome bond. But from what we know or can infer of their respective characters, it is by no means improbable that their relationship was to some extent a matter of business, that what really united them was the common interest of gain. By all accounts, Canaletto was of a whimsical and capricious disposition, exacting in his prices and unreliable in the delivery of promised work.[1] But neither was Smith quite the man to relish the blessedness of giving

---

[1] Count Tessin's letter of 16 June, 1736 (first quoted by Sirén, *Dessins et Tableaux de la Renaissance Italienne*, 1902, p. 107), describes him as *fantasque, bourru, Baptistisé*. No attempt has ever been made to interpret the last of these three epithets. It would seem that on the one hand it was a pun on *baptisé*, while on the other it alluded to someone of the name of Baptiste. Could this be the once celebrated and highly-paid flower-painter, Jean-Baptiste Monnoyer, 1636-1699, known as Baptiste? Could the word be intended to denote some point of resemblance to Baptiste, his popularity or successfulness, or perhaps some foible of his resulting from his success?

for its own sake. Though undoubtedly an enthusiast and a genuine lover of the arts, by the general disposition of his character and personality he hardly seems suited for the part of a Maecenas in the true sense. He was a merchant by training, by profession, and by habit of mind: would it be strange if he took something in return for what he gave? Is it a coincidence that we hear of him, late in life, making 'so much merit of giving himself the trouble' of performing a trivial service, that the person he favoured positively dreaded a recurrence of the obligation?[2] Count Tessin, writing in 1736, states categorically that for a term of four years Canaletto was engaged by Smith to work exclusively for him.[3] The fact remains, however, that neither for the years 1733/1736, nor for 1736/1739, can the Windsor Collection as we know it, that is to say Smith's collection, satisfactorily account for the entire output of an extremely prolific artist. Writing to Richard Bentley in 1754, Horace Walpole makes it perfectly clear that, in his belief, Smith 'purchased the fee-simple' of Canaletto for the express purpose of selling to the English; and Mary Berry, annotating this letter in 1798, is even more explicit, saying that he 'had engaged Canaletto for a certain number of years to paint exclusively for him, at a fixed price, and sold his pictures at an advanced price to English travellers.'[4] On the other hand, there is nothing to support, and much to contradict, the contention that Smith was anything in the nature of the *marchand amateur* of to-day—who treats his supposed private collection as stock-in-trade, and sells from it piecemeal as occasion arises. It may be, of course, that to some extent Smith's activities were confused with those of Owen McSwiney, who did certainly make a practice of retailing the works of the Venetian painters to English amateurs. But this explanation is hardly sufficient; and the impression remains that Smith was, in one way or another, financially interested in Canaletto's output, while himself remaining an insatiable collector of his work. We shall see that his position in Venice was such as to make the placing of commissions easy and profitable for all parties concerned. As to the ultimate sale of his own collection, it is a rather different aspect of his nature that will show itself in this connexion.

The type of collector, at once profit-seeking and idealistic, who is hopeful of disposing advantageously of his accumulated treasures, while earnestly desirous of keeping the work of his life intact, is to this day a frequent and familiar one. He tends to seek a compromise in selling his collection *en bloc*, and will find no difficulty insuperable, so long as there is the prospect of satisfying both his vanity and his purse. We have seen that in Smith the admirer and agent of Canaletto were perhaps none too harmoniously combined; it seems, moreover, that long before the date when the sale was actually effected, the impulse to build up the collection even more was at variance with a desire to be relieved of it. Without pursuing further the motives that prompted the vendor, still less attempting to analyse those of the purchaser, let us proceed to examine the transaction, by which George III became possessed not merely of a unique collection of Canaletto's work, but with it a wealth of other drawings, pictures and prints, and a multitude of books, to say nothing of such things as coins and gems. So much inaccuracy and contradiction has crept into the various accounts that have been given of the purchase at one time or another, that it will be best to start afresh and review the whole matter independently.

There can be little doubt that further documents bearing on this subject will in course of time come to light, and reward the student for patience and research. At the moment of writing only three main sources of information are available, and it is from these that all the essential facts must be extracted to produce a complete and consecutive account of the transaction. Most important of them is the will of Joseph Smith, signed and sealed by him at Venice on 5 April, 1761, and preserved

---

[2] *Letters of Lady Mary Montagu*, ed. W. M. Thomas, Vol. ii (1893), p. 319. [3] Tessin's letter of 1736; see above, note 1.
[4] *Works of Horace Walpole*, 1798, Vol. v, p. 297. It has been said erroneously that this allegation, that Smith sold Canalettos to English travellers, derived originally from Dallaway's notes to Walpole's *Anecdotes of Painting* (1862).

in the Archivio di Stato.[5] Next there is a letter from Smith to an unnamed addressee, dated 13 July, 1762, which is printed in Fortescue's *Correspondence of George III*,[6] and contains further essential information. Finally a receipt, preserved in duplicate in the British Museum,[7] bears the date of 28 January, 1763, and testifies in the autograph of Richard Dalton that he, Librarian to George III, had safely taken over that portion of the Smith collection which comprised the library. What emerges from these three documents and certain subsidiary sources is very briefly this: that as early as in 1756 negotiations for the sale had taken place, but been abandoned owing to the outbreak of the Seven Years War; that they had been resumed some time in the first half of 1762, or possibly a little earlier; that they were approaching completion by mid-summer, had been concluded by the autumn,[8] and by the beginning of 1763 were being formally implemented.

When in the spring of 1761 Smith drafted his last dispositions in the long and voluble document that is to yield information so important to our enquiry, Providence had in fact decreed that he should be spared for nearly ten more years of busy life. In 1770, when the will came to be proved and executed, it had become obsolete in one very essential respect: the large and valuable collections which in 1761 were still in the possession of the testator, and which formed the principal part of the estate of which he was disposing, had meanwhile been sold by his own negotiation; with the result that certain advice he had thought well to commit to paper, on the assumption that his widow would be 'minded to realize by selling' all or part of them, had become for all practical purposes unnecessary. It is, however, precisely these advisory clauses that have such interest and importance for the present enquiry. 'I was always desirous,' Smith writes, 'that some entire classes of my collection might remain united, such as my Library, Drawings, Gems, or Pictures, and with this view a treaty was commenced on the Part of a Royal Purchaser for my Library . . . but by reason of the present war breaking out about that time nothing was concluded.' These first negotiations of 1756 with 'a Royal Purchaser' (surely none other than George, Prince of Wales, though he is nowhere actually mentioned by name), involved a sum of 20,000 sequins, that is approximately £10,000, the Venetian *zecchino* then having a value of roughly half a guinea.

It is important to emphasize that the early negotiations, unlike the later, successful treaty, did not cover Smith's collections as a whole, but only that part of them comprising the library, for which the recently printed *Bibliotheca Smithiana* of 1755 served as the detailed specification. In it were included, however, not merely the printed books, but also the *Experimenta et Schedae* of Canaletto, along with the drawings of the Ricci, Visentini and others, all of which had been mounted in albums and incorporated in the library. In April, 1761, then, since the will makes no reference to renewed negotiations of sale, one can only infer either that the matter was still completely in abeyance, or that Smith was cautious enough to avoid mentioning what at the time was no more than a 'bird in the bush'.

Be that as it may, within little more than a year the situation had radically changed. For the substance of Smith's letter, already mentioned, of July 1762, is nothing less than the formal acceptance of terms of sale which had been foreshadowed in earlier, but no longer available correspondence, by which for a sum of £20,000, the '*whole* collection'—not merely the library—was to be 'removed to a more permanent & Glorious seat', and Smith was to have the 'utmost bound' of his ambition realized by seeing 'the work of his life' preserved entire.

---

[5] Published entire by H. F. Brown in *Notes and Queries*, 1905, pp. 282,383, and in extracts by L. Cust in *Burlington Magazine*, Vol. xxiii (1913), p. 150. See *Documents*, A (below, p. 59). [6] Vol. i (1921), No. 23. This letter was closely analysed by L. B. Namier in his *Additions and Corrections*, pp. 12, 13. See below, note 13. [7] Its existence only was mentioned by Mrs. H. F. Finberg, in *Walpole Society*, Vol. ix, p. 37. [8] The earliest reliable reference to the actual conclusion of the deal is in a letter of 16 October, 1762, quoted in F.A. Barnard's introduction to *Bibliothecae Regiae Catalogus*, 1820, Vol. i, p. viii.

This letter enables us to infer a great deal more than the general trend of events. Though filled with the conventional phrases of politeness, with solemn declarations of the writer's veracity and probity, and above all of his desire to be 'freed from the mortifying suspicion of being even thought minded to drive a Bargain', it shows clearly that it was Smith who in the first place approached his correspondent and asked his help; and that it was to him, the anonymous recipient of the letter, that Smith owed the 'kind ingerency' of the proposed transaction—by which is meant, no doubt, the favour of bringing it to the sympathetic attention of the King. But it makes it clear, too, that it was the person addressed in the letter who, after being told by Smith what he considered to be the 'real value' of the collections, advised him to compound for a sum of £20,000; and to that sum Smith now agrees, surely not unwillingly, though of course with protestations that his chief concern is to satisfy the Royal purchaser, and that from any other 'the double' would be worth less.

The exact terms of payment proposed in Smith's letter provided for an initial and immediate instalment of £10,000, payable by bills of exchange, this to be followed at intervals of a year by three further payments, each of one-third of the remaining sum with 5 per cent. interest added. What was actually carried out was slightly different, but not to the disadvantage of the vendor. From the detailed accounts of expenditure of the Civil List, published in the *Journal of the House of Commons* in 1770,[9] at which date George III was petitioning Parliament for the payment of his debts, it appears (under the heading of 'Secret and Special Service') that not only was the initial £10,000 duly remitted in the financial year 1762/63 through the banking firm of Messrs. Udny in Venice, but that the transaction was completed in 1763/4 by a further such payment to a total of £10,805 6s. 6d.—the odd amount covering no doubt the interest and brokerage, and possibly also the incidental expenses of package and transport. From another letter, which need not concern us in detail,[10] a letter addressed to a Treasury official on 15 May, 1763, by Smith's mediator in England, it appears that Smith had been worried about the security offered him for the outstanding money; whereupon his friend and protector, being anxious to 'stand clear with the old Gentleman', urged despatch in winding the matter up, once and for all.

We shall need to pause longer over the last of our three principal documents—the receipt drafted and signed at Venice by the Royal Librarian, on 28 January, 1763, duplicate versions of which, both holograph, are appended to copies of the printed catalogue of Smith's library. How it comes about that both these books should belong to what is now known as the King's Library[11]—the nucleus of which is none other than Smith's library purchased by George III and handed over by his successor to the British Museum—how it is that they did not remain in Smith's hands, since they are receipts covering not the buyer, but the seller, is hard to understand. Whatever the explanation may be, we learn that, though Smith had expressed himself in his letter of 1762 willing to attend personally to the despatch of the collections to England, it was thought advisable that Dalton should journey to Venice and take over custody on the spot. The wording of his receipt is rather involved (and in one respect ambiguous[12]), but its main point at least is perfectly clear: Dalton testifies to the safe receipt, 'all in perfect good order', of the collection of books as listed in the printed catalogue—the library, that is, which included Canaletto's *Experimenta et Schedae* and the other similar albums. The receipt does not, however, cover the other sections of the collection, and we must suppose either that they were separately receipted at the time, or that for the present only the library

[9] Vol. xxxii, pp. 546, 555. [10] British Museum, Add. MS. 38200. ff. 332-3. [11] Pressmarks 123. e. 10 and 823. h. 26.
[12] The ambiguity lies in the conflicting phrases 'part of his collection' and 'the whole collection'; see below *Documents*, p. 62. The letter referred to in note 8 contains the passage '. . . there has been purchased . . . *all the Museum* of Mr. Smith . . . consisting of his Library, Prints, Drawings, Coins and Gems'. There is no mention of pictures. For R. Hayward's note of March, 1763, referring to 'Mr. Smith of Venice his Collection of Pictures, Books, & sold to His Majesty', see *Walpole Society*, Vol. ix, p. 24, note 1.

was formally taken over, an assumption that would be reasonable enough, since the initial payment was for £10,000, and the abortive negotiations of 1756 had specified precisely that sum to cover the library as a single unit. The matter is of little importance. What is of far greater interest is that Dalton, by mentioning the Rt. Hon. James Stuart Mackenzie as the person of authority under whose orders he acted, solves once and for all the riddle of the negotiator of the sale, the unnamed addressee of Smith's letter of 1762.[13] Again, it does more than satisfy our idle curiosity; it virtually discloses how the negotiations, broken off in 1756, came to be renewed, and why they now developed so swiftly and successfully. Between 1758 and 1761 Mackenzie had been stationed at Turin as British Minister to the Court of Sardinia, and somewhere in Italy and about that time Smith had apparently come to be on friendly terms with him. Mackenzie was the younger brother of John Stuart, third Earl of Bute, a close personal friend of the King, and his adviser both in matters of politics and culture. Long before the earliest date to which the renewed negotiations can definitely be traced back—5 May, 1762—Bute's influence stood very high, and his brother must in consequence have been an extremely useful ally to have. But within three weeks of that day, the situation had further improved overnight, and taken an even more propitious aspect. On 26 May, 1762, Bute, not unexpectedly, rose to be Lord of the Treasury, and for about a year, during which he retained his office as the King's first Minister of State, his authority was at its zenith. If in 1756 Smith could justly have complained of the political developments of the day, he had no such cause in 1762. Whether or not he had anticipated this particular development, the moment for renewing the negotiations could hardly have been more shrewdly timed.

Having now said something of Smith's personal relations to Canaletto, and the circumstances of the sale of his collections, let us deal briefly with the man himself and his unusual, colourful, gifted, but not altogether sympathetic personality. In consequence of a very inadequate notice in the *Dictionary of National Biography*, the events of his life are for the most part as inaccurately recorded as his character is imperfectly realized.[14]

The date of his birth, though often stated to be 1682, must in fact have been as early as 1676, or possibly even 1674, if the registers are to be literally believed which declare that at his death, in 1770, he had attained an age of 96 years or thereabouts. His lineage is unknown, and of his early youth all that can be said is that he was a scholar of Westminster[15], a fact which stood him in good stead, and indeed 'crowned the recommendation', when in 1740 the Duke of Richmond sponsored him for the chief appointment of his life, that of His Majesty's Consul to the Serene Republic of Venice. We do not know exactly when he first settled in that city, but it is generally assumed to have been in the early years of the eighteenth century; and then it was certainly in his lifelong capacity as a merchant. He became apprenticed, it seems, to Thomas Williams, the Consul of the time,[16] and it appears that he was somehow to blame, as the result of an 'error, neglect, or mismanagement', for the latter's 'failure'. It was not, however, on this occasion that Smith himself was nominated to the post. His immediate predecessor was Neil Brown, at whose death on 29 June, 1740, he found himself in a position of sufficient authority at the Consulate to take over as deputy, and to seal up all papers left by the deceased which seemed to be of an official nature. But long before that, Smith

[13]On different evidence altogether (viz. the letter in the British Museum quoted in note 10) L. B. Namier has already reached the conclusion that the recipient of Smith's letter of 1762 must have been Stuart Mackenzie. See *Additions and Corrections to Fortescue's Correspondence of George III*, 1939, pp. 12, 13. [14]Many important additions to the D. N. B. were made by H. F. Brown in *Notes and Queries*, 1905, pp. 221ff, and by J. B. Whitmore, P. H. Emden, and H. F. Finberg, *ibidem*, vol. 186, 1944, pp. 154, 207, 255/6. [15]See letter of the Duke of Richmond to the Duke of Newcastle, 31 August, 1740 (British Museum, Add. MS. 32,694, f. 544). It is quoted by J. B. Whitmore, *The Elizabethan*, March 1947, p. 87. [16]Smith speaks of him in clause XI of his will (below, p. 59) as 'my Predecessor'. If Williams was really Consul, as the phrase would imply, it was presumably between about 1716 and 1723, that is, after Hugh Broughton and before Neil Brown.

must have risen to a position of importance and affluence; and this may have been the result, to some extent, of his marriage, in or about 1710—a rich if thoroughly unsatisfactory one.

As in the incident of Thomas Williams, it is hard to close one's eyes to something rather discreditable about Smith's first matrimonial alliance. The first Mrs. Smith was none other than the celebrated operatic singer, Katherine Tofts, who, after a short but brilliant career at Drury Lane and the Haymarket—during which the 'sweet silver tone of her voice' and her 'fine proportioned figure' proved more than a match for her redoubtable rival, Francesca de l'Épine—retired about 1709 to Venice with a large fortune, but in a state of health bordering on intermittent insanity. For the many years she still had to live, *diutino vexata morbo*, she was kept, it is said, under more or less permanent restraint.

Not till 1740, the year in which Smith was appointed Consul, did he purchase (and afterwards rebuild) the palace on the Grand Canal, which the visitor still associates with him and his collections, drastically altered though it is to-day. Now known as the Palazzo Mangilli-Valmarana, it stands in the *contrada* of the SS. Apostoli, not far from the Rialto and directly opposite the Pescheria. But long before he bought it, Smith had been its occupant on leasehold from a member of the Balbi family; and there can be no doubt that it was there (and at a villa at Mogliano, the retreat of his *villeggiature* and leisure hours) that the collections accumulated, and became, as the Président de Brosses wrote in 1739, one of the sights of the city not to be missed by the cultured traveller. Smith himself indicates 1720 as the approximate date of the beginning of his activity as a collector. Though books were the first and dominating passion of his life, he soon combined with this the enthusiasms of an art-collector of catholic taste. It is to his credit that in both branches his interests embraced the past as well as the present. If as a connoisseur he appreciated the contemporary schools, he was not insensitive to those of earlier date; if as a bibliophile a rare edition was irresistible to him, he also fostered the production of books, and gave the backing of his wealth and enterprise to the firm of publishers well-known to posterity under the imprint of G. B. Pasquali. His crowded life of those years was certainly, by and large, a contented and very successful one; but we know of one incident that doubtless struck a bitter blow to his pride. A letter has been preserved[17] showing that in 1752 he had hopes of promotion from the Consulate to the Residency, even at the price of divesting himself entirely of 'the name and Business of a Merchant'. In this, however, his ambition was frustrated, and it was John Murray, his future brother-in-law, who was appointed to the more dignified and responsible post.

A widower at the ripe age of some eighty years, Smith lost no time in contemplating matrimony afresh. The quest of another bride, however, was not immediately successful. The recollections and letters of Justiniana Wynne, afterwards Countess Orsini-Rosenberg,[18] make it clear that at a crucial stage in the life of that *grande amoureuse*, he had serious hopes of winning her hand. His suit, however, did not prosper and was finally abandoned. It was only then that Smith consoled himself with the sister of his successful rival for the post of Resident. Lady Mary Montagu wrote in 1758:[19] 'he has lately married Murray's sister, a beauteous virgin of forty, who after having refused all the peers in England because the nicety of her conscience would not permit her to give her hand where her heart was untouched, she remained without a husband till the charms of that fine gentleman, Mr. Smith, who is only eighty-two, determined her to change her mind.' This is then the wife to whom, in his will of 1761, the ex-consul (he retired in 1760) gave the solicitous advice on the sale of the collections, with which we have already had occasion to deal. The link with Murray is revealing. 'Such a scandalous fellow', says Lady Mary, 'in every sense of the word, he is not to be trusted to

[17]British Museum, Add. MS. 32, 834, f. 133. [18]*Moral and Sentimental Essays*, 1785, Vol. i, p. 55; Bruno Brunelli, *Un' Amica del Casanova*, 1923, *passim*. [19]*Letters*, ed. 1893, Vol. ii, p. 319.

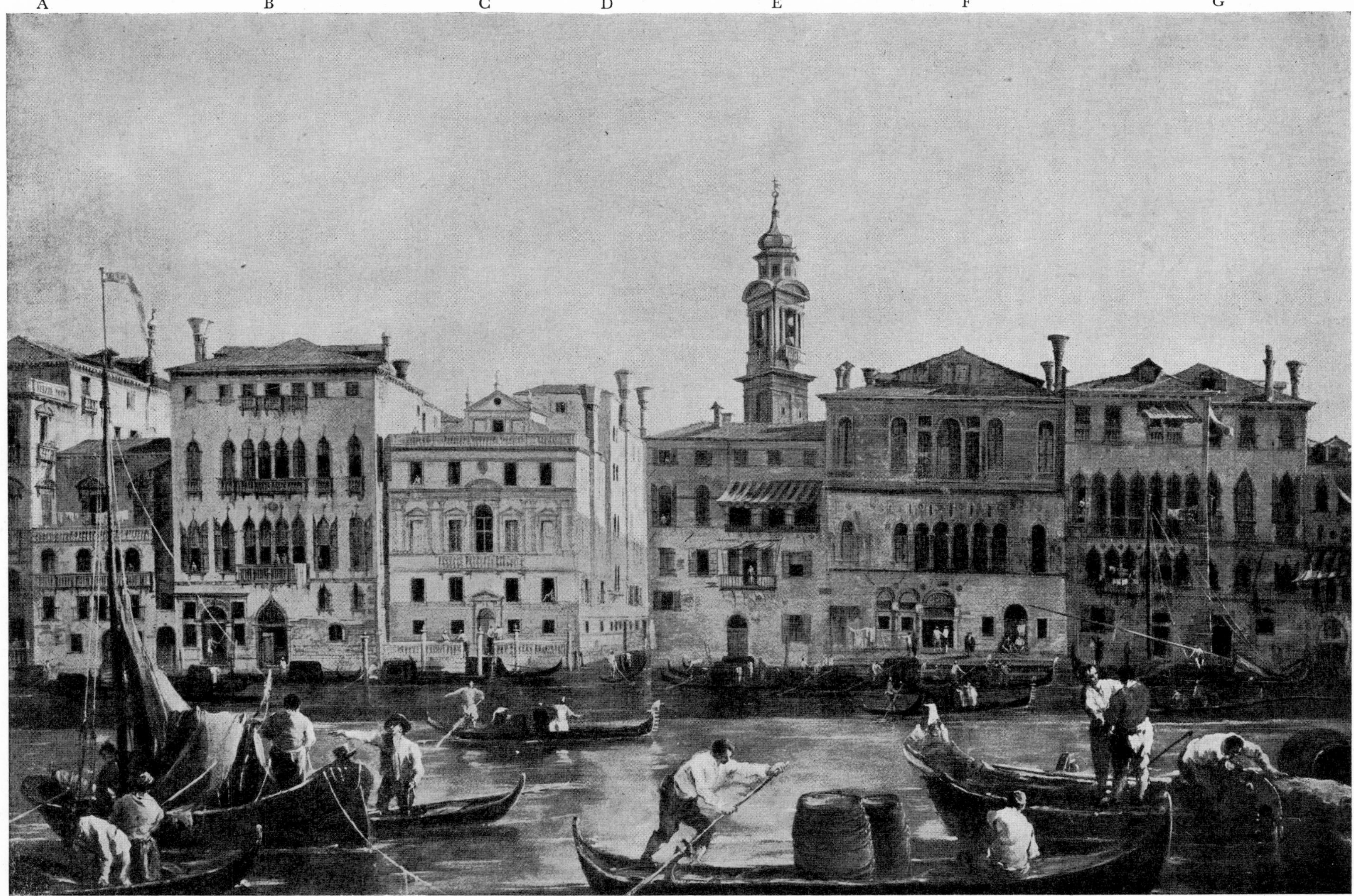

FIG. I. CONSUL SMITH'S HOUSE ON THE GRAND CANAL, FROM A PAINTING (? AT AUGSBURG) IN THE STYLE OF GUARDI

A. Palazzo Michiel dalle Colonne. B. Palazzo Michiel 'del Brusà'. C. Consul Smith's house (now Palazzo Mangilli-Valmarana) showing the unaltered façade by Antonio Visentini. D. Rio SS.Apostoli. E. The campanile of SS. Apostoli. F. Cà da Mosto (Albergo del Lion Bianco). G. Casa Dolfin

change a sequin, despised by the Government for his smuggling, which was his original profession, and always surrounded with pimps and brokers, who are his privy councillors'. So, too, in the most colourful memoirs of the day, those of Giacomo Casanova, we meet Smith on occasion in very doubtful company,—as an accessory, for example, to the plottings of his brother-in-law and Count Capsocefalo to seduce the beautiful nun 'M.M.' from the embraces of that notorious libertine.

One further detail of interest may be drawn from the letter of 1762. It was then Smith's intention to 'terminate his concerns' in Venice, and to return to London as soon as the treaty of sale had been concluded. Whether he ever saw England again or not, this much is certain: it was in Venice, and the parish of the SS. Apostoli,[20] that, in 1770, death in the guise of 'senile fever' at last overtook him. His wish to be buried in the Protestant cemetery of S. Nicolo al Lido was duly carried out; in 1786 Goethe crossed the lagoon and identified the grave, but found it so nearly concealed under drifted sand that he remarked it would soon disappear from sight altogether.[21] To-day the spot where Smith was buried, and Goethe stood, is concealed not by sand, but by the concrete run-ways of the Lido air-port; and only a laudable act of piety has preserved the gravestone in a modern cemetery near-by. Most of the inscription on it is still clearly legible, but the *stemma*, Smith's rather pretentiously blazoned coat-of-arms, is in a bad state of decay. *Argent on two chevrons sable, six fleurs-de-lys of the field*, are practically obliterated; *on a chief azure, a lion passant argent* has an outline so crumbled as to be scarcely recognizable.

Walpole's caustic characterization of the 'Merchant of Venice', as he calls him, and reference to the 'title-page of his understanding', the cruel analysis of a rather superficial mind with higher pretensions, are too well known to be quoted again, and yet too apposite to be passed over in silence. It is worth mentioning, however, in this connexion, that Smith was not wholly unconscious of his limitations. He described himself once as a 'middling genius',[22] and the very phrase has genius in it of a sort. But it is only too evident that there was something contradictory in his character, something incompatible which 'middling' well conveys. A collector in a big way, yet a keen salesman; a patron of the arts, yet not averse to profit. A bookman, certainly, but not effectively a scholar; *un signorone*, no doubt, but not strictly a gentleman.

To return to Canaletto, after this long digression on the collection and its collector, it will be well to start by saying a few words on the probable date of his first contacts with Smith. Unlike the case of the Ricci, where much useful information is at our disposal, here, with Canaletto, the available evidence is meagre, and the inquiry leads to no very positive result. It is little help to know that in 1735 a series of views of the Grand Canal, painted for and owned by Smith, were published as engravings by Antonio Visentini. For even if ample time is allowed for their execution, first by the painter and then by the engraver, this could hardly take us back to a date before, say, 1730.
7-11 A drawing at Darmstadt, which connects closely with what is apparently an early group at Windsor,
1-6 bears an authentic date of 1729. Another group at Windsor, broad and summary in handling, and a set of pictures related to it, may reasonably be assumed to be a year or two earlier. But even so, we have only felt our way backwards, and none too securely at that, to a date somewhere about 1727—the year in which Owen McSwiney wrote to the Duke of Richmond that Canaletto had more work on hand than he could readily cope with; even so we are still in doubt whether Smith was really one of the earliest clients of the artist, who, in 1720, is already known to have established himself as a specialist in Venetian topographical painting.

---

[20] Presumably, therefore, in the palace he had lived in so long. Brunelli states that it was sold by his widow in 1775 to Caterina da Mula Pisani. [21] *Italienische Reise*, ed. Graevenitz, 1912, p. 49. [22] In the letter referred to in note 17, Simonson (*Francesco Guardi*, 1904, p. 18) connects it with Smith's candidature for the post of *Consul*.

FIG.2. CANALETTO: S. MARIA DELLA SALUTE FROM THE PIAZZETTA (WINDSOR CASTLE)

The fact is that neither the opening nor concluding phase of Canaletto's activity as a draughtsman is represented in the Windsor collection. Whatever the personal relations of Smith and Canaletto may have been as their lives drew to a close, it is obvious that the latest possible date for any of the Windsor drawings must be the date when the collection was sold; and it follows that the period between 1763 and 1768 (in which year Canaletto, though nearly a generation younger than Smith, predeceased his friend) cannot be represented either. Thus it will be useless to look for any counterpart to the well-known Hamburg drawing of 1766, which was signed by the artist with the special remark that he had made it at the age of 68, and without spectacles; or even to that sumptuous series of ceremonial subjects relating to the investiture of Doge Alvise Mocenigo in 1763, which certain modern writers have so unjustly rejected.[23] Six drawings in the collection are of London views, which implies a date not earlier than 1746, the year when Canaletto first came to England, while some of them must for topographical reasons be as late as about 1750/1. But whether his post-English period, or rather that portion of it between his return to Venice about 1755 and the sale of the collection in 1762, is represented, can only be established in the light of stylistic evidence. With Canaletto this criterion is never an easy or accurate one; the mannerisms of his figure drawing in particular, the rounded calligraphy so characteristic of his penwork, is noticeable long before the concluding phase of his activity. In at least one case, however—the large architectural composition
141 reproduced in our penultimate plate—the whole conception so closely resembles that of the *prospettiva* which the artist submitted as his diploma picture after admission to the Venetian Academy in 1763, that its date cannot be very much earlier. It would seem, therefore, that this drawing, and possibly others akin to it, were almost certainly incorporated in the collection after the failure of the first negotiations of sale, and probably not long before their final resumption.

Though mounted to-day as separate items, Smith's Canaletto drawings were contained originally in a large, elaborately tooled, leather-bound album, as those of the Ricci, Visentini and others still are. Inserted in each of these albums is, or was, a loose slip giving in Italian a list of the contents. That of the Canaletto volume is preserved,[24] though the album itself was dismembered, and in it are listed, in addition to a frontispiece now lost (no doubt one of Visentini's daintily coloured designs), a total of 139 drawings, 21 original etchings, and two further engravings of London views after paintings of which the originals belonged to Smith. Against this figure of 139 drawings, Detlev von Hadeln speaks of 140, but in fact catalogues 141, whereas the actual total to-day is 143, two being on mounts of larger size than the rest. This leaves four items to be accounted for. It is not without interest to observe that from the Visentini album three drawings have been abstracted, which had been pasted in by a method different from the rest,[25] and below which Canaletto's name had subsequently been inscribed. The discrepancy, however, between the total in the list and that in the present collection, cannot be accounted for by this, for there would still be one drawing too many; and, moreover, there are no visible traces to be found in the Canaletto series, as we now have it, of any method of mounting other than Smith's usual one. It remains uncertain, therefore, what has become of the supposed

---

[23]Hadeln lists only the drawing formerly in the Henry Oppenheimer Collection. Those in the British Museum (for reproductions, see *Country Life*, 7 Oct., 1922) he condemns, though an item as worthless as 1895.9.15.862 finds favour in his eyes. Two further items of the Mocenigo series, unknown to Hadeln, belong to Lord Rosebery. The whole series was engraved by Brustolon, but not necessarily from the very drawings aforesaid. Nothing would be more natural than that a series so important should have been repeated by the hand of the Master himself. [24]See *Documents* D, below, p. 62.

[25]These were fixed to the pages by means of dabs of adhesive, whereas Smith's normal method was to apply paste all around the edges. This pasting along the edges shows itself, unaccountably, in two different ways. The more frequent is that the white tone of the paper extends as far as the pasted strip, which latter shows a distinctly yellowish tone. But in the case of Nos. 1-6, and elsewhere, the centre of the drawing shows what almost seems like a yellowish stain over its surface, while the pasted edge is appreciably lighter. The only explanation that can be offered is that different pastes reacted differently on papers of different quality. The same may be observed in the Visentini volume: e.g., 7626, which shows a yellowish edge and white centre, while 7566/74 show the yellowish centre and white edge.

FIG. 3. CANALETTO: PIAZZA DI S. MARCO, FACING S. GEMINIANO (WINDSOR CASTLE)

Canalettos detached from the Visentini volume, and why it is that the series as we see it to-day is four items in excess of the total recorded on the slip. It may simply be, of course, that an error was made in the counting, or that Smith was able to add to the collection after the counting was made. In the latter event it would be reasonable to suppose that the supernumerary items were the latest in execution.

Trivial as it may appear, the point is interesting to this extent, that this discrepancy in numbers to some extent invalidates the virtual guarantee of genuineness that Smith's ownership would otherwise carry with it.[26] But for this, the student would feel himself bound to an almost blind acceptance of the whole series. Seldom was anyone in a better position to acquire a collection of unimpeachable authenticity. Smith knew all that we do not know of the activities of the Canaletto workshop, and having himself once contrived a reprint of a rare Boccaccio, which was almost indistinguishable from the original, he must have been sufficiently on his guard against deception. Even to play with the idea, as Cust did,[27] of attributing to Bellotto the more monotonously executed line drawings,

[26]This is said with cognizance of the fact that Ricci's *Finding of Moses* was wrongly listed in Smith's inventory as by P. Veronese (Burlington House Exhibition, 1946/47, No. 414). The inventory contains another strange misstatement, inaccuracy, or what you will: the assertion that Canaletto's original drawings for the paintings engraved in Visentini's series of 1735 are in the 'collection of designs'. In point of fact they are not.

[27]*Burlington Magazine*, Vol. xxiii (1913), p. 275.

would be to undermine one's faith without real cause; to subscribe to it would be to cut adrift irresponsibly from what is as firm an anchorage as one could ever wish to have.

74 Of the six drawings listed by Hadeln as authentically signed, only one is in the Windsor Collection. An autograph inscription, *Antonio Canale*, occurs on the back, and thus it would be vouched for even were its authenticity less obvious than it is. In point of fact, however, no less than seven other drawings at Windsor bear signatures equally authentic, though of a different and more cryptic kind. It
50/1, 108, was overlooked by Hadeln, not only at Windsor but in various other collections, and not only on
130/1, 140/1 drawings but also on certain etchings, and in at least one case on a picture, that a small and sometimes quite inconspicuously placed coat-of-arms, charged with a chevron, has the full validity of a normal signature. A particularly interesting example is on a drawing formerly in the collection of Sir Robert Mond,[28] where it occurs no less than three times as part of an elaborate architectural design. It is, not unnaturally, in more or less fanciful settings that the sign is almost invariably found, and the one case known to us of its use in a painting[29] conforms to the general rule. But why it should occur so seldom in pictures cannot satisfactorily be explained, unless it resolves itself simply into this: that if minded to sign a picture at all, Canaletto would do so either with his name in full, or in abbreviation, which was not his practice as a draughtsman. There are other such differences of convention between the drawings and paintings; the flocks of flying birds, for example, which are so frequently noticeable in the drawings, are in the paintings almost invariably omitted. Broadly speaking, the chevron signature is an indication of the master's middle or later period; but its occurrence among the etchings, where it was first observed by Helmuth Fritzsche,[30] is evidence of its dating back at least to the early 'forties. The chevron itself is explained by the fact that the artist was descended from the noble Venetian family da Canal, two branches of which, according to such authorities as Coronelli and Freschot, displayed it in their coats—*argent a chevron azure* and *azure a chevron or*. It has been a consistent tradition among writers on Canaletto to imply some doubt as to the legitimacy of his claim to patrician origin; but the objection is frivolous and lacks any real support. And moreover, if the claim had been a false one, is it not strange that it never was challenged at the time, or escaped the official vigilance of the *Avvogadori*? Zanetti, himself a patrician, mentioned the relationship in connexion with Antonio's father, within a few years of the date of the death of the son. Nor did the artist merely lay claim to the arms. In the title below his portrait engraving in the *Prospectus Magni Canalis* of 1735, the specific phrase *origine civis Venetus* occurs, while Visentini's portrait alongside is simply styled *Venetus*. It must be for the genealogist, if anyone, to carry the enquiry further. So far as the general historian is concerned, the chevron signature has every claim to be recognized as valid and heraldically correct.

In a collection as abundant as that under consideration, there is naturally much to be learnt about the draughtsman's technique, and it might be tempting to run to some length on this subject. For the sake of brevity, a convenient starting point is Hadeln's statement—true no doubt as far as it goes, but certainly over-simplified—that 'the instrument with which Canaletto draws is the pen'. Even at a glance it must be noticeable that the texture of his pen-work varies greatly; there are, to be exact, three fairly distinct types, and it seems natural to assume, though it cannot be proved, that each of these corresponds with a different type of pen. The quill was, of course, the normal pen of

---

[28]This drawing, moreover, has the artist's name written in small letters between the lower margin and border-line, a type of 'signature' which, in general, is not at all reassuring. It occurs throughout the series of small Roman views in the British Museum (see below, p. 50); and in the same collection on 1866. 7.14.16 (the mis-named *Palazzo Gradenigo*, which also has the chevron); and on 1910. 2.12.22 (similar to a drawing, also 'signed', formerly in the Lanna Collection). On the other hand, its occurrence is noted on Count Anton Seilern's magnificent *S. Giacomo di Rialto* (from the Leslie Collection), and the *capriccio*, *Burl. Mag.* xlii, p. 251. [29]The Windsor *capriccio* of the Scala dei Giganti, No. 474 of the 1946/47 Exhibition at Burlington House. Here it occurs in conjunction with a *normal* signature. [30]*Graphische Künste, Mittlg.*, 1930, p. 50.

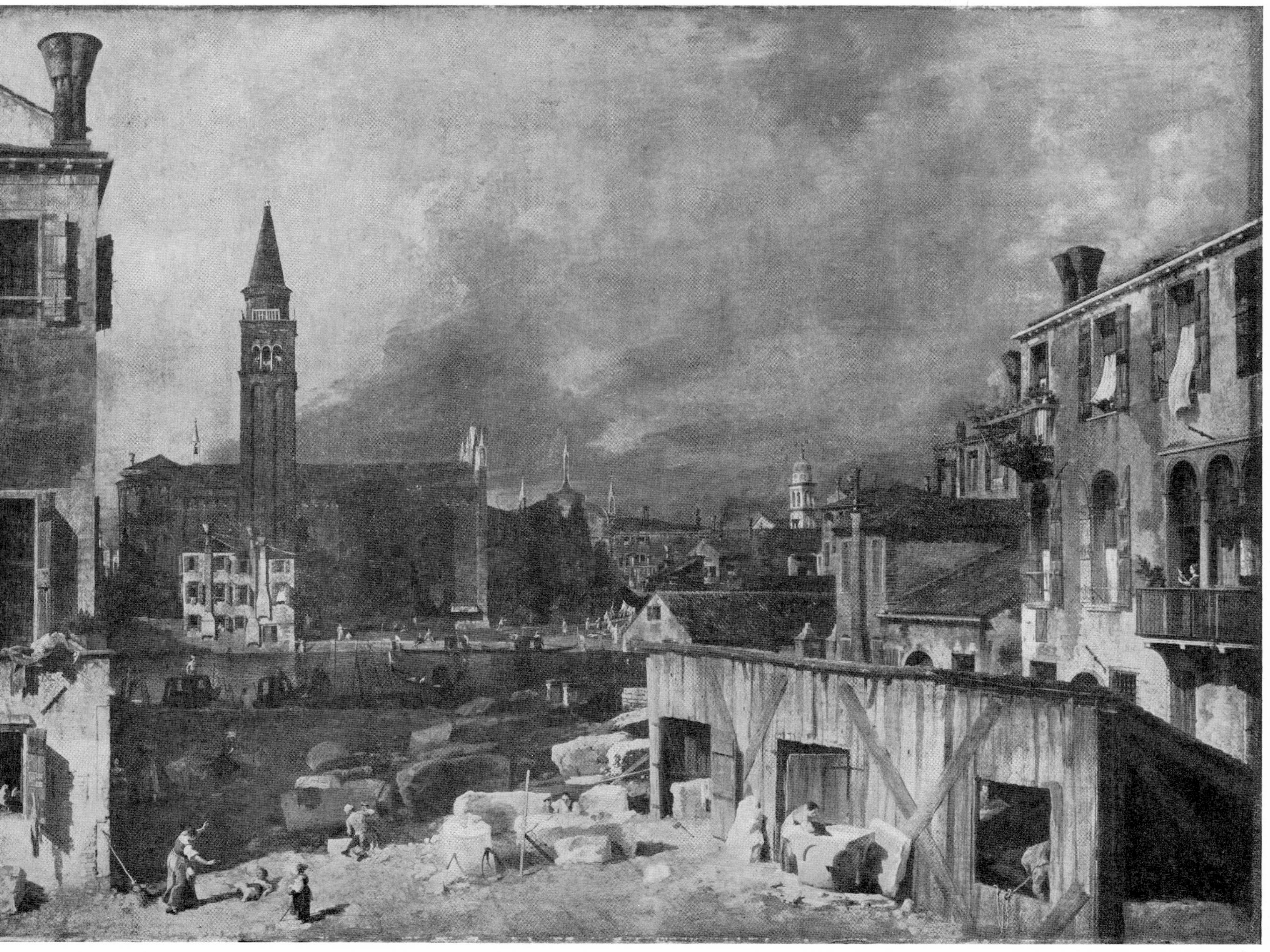

FIG. 4. CANALETTO: THE STONEMASON'S YARD (CAMPO S. VIDAL) (NATIONAL GALLERY)

the day. Of quills, however, there was a considerable variety—goose, turkey, swan, raven, peacock, and crow;[31] their properties varied, and there were various methods of dressing them for use, even before the individual skill of the scribe or draughtsman came into play, in cutting them to suit his purpose. There was the reed pen, too, as old as time, and it seems highly probable that Canaletto used it when occasion demanded—though it must be admitted that one of the softer quills, if broadly cut and subjected to prolonged pressure, might yield an almost indistinguishable effect. But in contrast to the effects of quill and reed, palpable in some cases, less obvious in others, there is an abundance of thin, incisive line-work in Canaletto's drawings, which can only be described as having a metallic quality. This leads us admittedly into the field of conjecture. Of the metal pen far less is known than of the others, though it is certain that in antiquity a form of bronze pen, split at the point, was used, and occasional evidence confirms its existence through the Middle Ages and later. The commercialized metal nib was of course a blessing bestowed on us by Birmingham and the nineteenth century; but there is good reason to believe that even in Canaletto's day some sort of steel point was no longer uncommon. In the opinion of the present writer, Canaletto himself must have recognized its merits and kept it in constant use. If in the ensuing Catalogue abbreviations are introduced simply to denote the *apparent effect* of quill, reed or metal, this is with the intention of avoiding a dogmatic pronouncement, since the precise nature of the materials employed remains, when all is said and done, conjectural.[32]

But it was not with the pen that Canaletto began his drawings. If on the last head Hadeln's description has shown itself to be somewhat inadequate, on this other, on the subject of the preliminary indications over which the artist's pen or pens had subsequently to work, his remarks, so far as the Windsor drawings are concerned, are nothing short of misleading. In some two or three random cases he mentions that a preliminary sketching-in with pencil is visible. The truth is that in the vast majority of the drawings, whether slight or finished, whether purely linear or elaborated with wash, the pencil foundation is there, even though it may not always be obvious. Nor is this preliminary work restricted entirely to free-hand drawing. Unlike Guardi, Canaletto made a fairly consistent practice of indicating the leading verticals of his architecture with pencil and ruler; not infrequently, too, the oblique lines of the perspective and the horizon extending across the page from margin to margin. The ruler, moreover, is frequently used in conjunction with pen and ink, and produces a certain effect of neatness and precision, which is in contrast to Guardi's more painter-like approach—Guardi was in fact more sensitive to the apparent instability of Venetian architecture. It has repeatedly been emphasized that the use of red chalk is exceptional, and essentially this is true, though the point has perhaps been rather overstated. From the Windsor Collection at least
71 one example of his middle period can be cited where it is extensively used; and it is equally obvious in the Ashmolean figure-studies, which are of very early date, and in the Mocenigo series, which is late. For minor indications other than those of form, such as horizon-lines and the like, the use of red chalk is not uncommon, though it needs an attentive eye to detect it. In the same way, close and patient scrutiny is required to observe what was really one of Canaletto's most habitual tricks, a practice which for want of a better term will be described in our Catalogue as pin-pointing. While Bellotto and other copyists used the ruled pencil verticals in exactly the same way as the Master himself, it has yet to be proved that pin-pointing was other than a habit peculiarly his own. The purpose of it seems simply to have been to plot the principal points and distances of an architectural composition, before beginning it in ink; and it does not seem likely that the process involved

---

[31] Sylvia Groves in *Country Life*, 30 November, 1945, p. 954. [32] The sequence of the abbreviations, Q, R, and M, will not be intended to indicate either the priority or preponderance of one type over the other. It should be emphasized, moreover, that no expression will be given to any element of doubt that there may be.

FIG. 5. CANALETTO: CANALE DI S. CHIARA (FORMERLY AT LANGLEY PARK, SLOUGH)

FIG. 6. CANALETTO: VIEW OF MESTRE. ETCHING (CF. CAT. NO. 89)

anything in the nature of a transfer. What is visible is no more than a series of minute perforations, more or less numerous, and anything from a needle to a dividers'-point may have been used to produce it. The dividers, incidentally, were in constant use by Canaletto, and anyone with good eyesight, and a wish to strain it to no very useful purpose, can observe the traces of the instrument in countless drawings, in the preliminary incising of arches and domes.

There remains much of essential interest concerning Canaletto's habits as a draughtsman, about which little or nothing can be said with certainty. What proportion of the drawings which have the appearance of exact views were in fact done on the spot, with the actual scene before his eyes? How many of the great Windsor series agree with the story of Dr. John Hinchliffe, who described how he 'chanced to see a little man making a sketch of the Campanile', and recognized him as the famous Canaletto in person?[33] Which, if any, were done with the *camera optica*, as witnessed by Zanetti and other contemporaries? How many are derived even indirectly from such mechanically aided drawings, that is to say based on 'cameragraphs', though themselves drawn freehand?

To decide whether a drawing was made from nature, only one criterion can effectively be applied: the purely subjective consideration whether it has the convincing freshness, the manifest immediacy that one would naturally expect.[34] Having regard to the fact that Canaletto was adept at

[33]Quoted by Mrs. H. F. Finberg, *Walpole Society*, Vol. ix, p. 44. See also a recent letter in *The Times* (18 September, 1947), disclosing the present whereabouts of the drawing to which Hinchliffe referred. It belongs to Lady Annabel Crewe. Its date (1760), and the fact that it was from nature, being vouched for, it is clearly of special interest in the present context. [34]An interesting observation is that of Ashby and Constable (*Burlington Magazine*, xlvi (1925), p. 293), who claim to observe a systematic raising of the horizon-line in the drawings of more elaborate finish.

feigning such immediacy, even when there was demonstrably none, the writer is personally of the
belief that of the *vedute esatte* the proportion which can be claimed as such with any real certainty,
is by no means overwhelming. Palpably from nature are those early, brilliantly swift sketches of
almost Guardiesque character; certain truly sensitive views of the Grand Canal; the peculiarly 7-11, 17-21
atmospheric *S. Chiara* and *Salute;* and to quote instances of the combined use of line and wash, the 13, 53,
exquisite pair of *S. Elena.* On the other hand, one will without hesitation reject the claim for all the 67, 68
Roman subjects, and for the rather tedious series of Venetian churches. There are, of course, many 32-36;
more that are no less certainly in the one category or the other; but the issue cannot by any means 102-113
always be decided.

Among the open-air studies already mentioned, some pretty certainly served as the basis of
pictures; and the same is true of certain other drawings, whose summary execution might be 1-4
mistaken for the brevity of out-door sketches, but which were more probably made from memory,
with the purpose of exploring the compositional effect of pictures planned by the artist. In most other
cases of correspondence, however, between picture and drawing, the resemblance seems to be of a
purely outward nature, that is to say merely topographical and without any further interest or significance attaching to it. In fact, Canaletto's draughtsmanship was to a great extent an independent
practice, meeting an independent commercial demand on his output; and the question of priority
between a painted version of a composition and a drawing should never in his case be answered on
the common assumption that the simpler medium and smaller size came first. On the other hand,
in several cases where an identical composition occurs both as a line drawing and as a drawing in
line and wash, the former seems invariably to have preceded the latter. This may be inferred from
certain quite unimportant *pentimenti*, to which the Catalogue will in due course refer. 46/7; 135/6

The frontispiece of Canaletto's etchings describes in the artist's own terms the two main types of his *vedute*, whether drawn or painted or etched. It differentiates between *vedute prese da i luoghi, or* faithful delineations of actual places, and *vedute ideate*, or imaginary views. Synonymous with the former expression are such others as *veduta esatta* or *dal naturale*; the latter type is equally well described as *alla pittoresca* or *di fantasia*. But we find the two types merging capriciously one into the other, and so yet another term of classification, the *capriccio*, becomes essential to the Canaletto vocabulary. *Capriccio* did not mean to him, however, exactly what it meant to his contemporaries, Piranesi, Tiepolo and Guardi, with each of whom the term partakes of an individual flavour. It always suggests, of course, an escape from reality, an unfettered play of the imagination. With Tiepolo and Guardi the prevailing note is essentially and exquisitely lyrical (the former peopling his compositions with strange orientals, warriors, philosophers and *lazzaroni*, the latter inventing landscapes of a dreamlike limpidity), while with Piranesi, on the other hand, it is always dramatic, and often, indeed, menacing. As to Canaletto, his caprice, in its truest expression, reflects yet another
mood. No doubt some few of his works are *capricci* almost in Guardi's sense. But the real Canaletto 131/2
capriccio is as prosaic as Pannini's; its wit consists in an incongruous juxtaposition of realistic motives of topography, motives that remain obviously, indeed provocatively, unrelated. It sets the Colleoni beside the Colosseum, raises the dome of St. Peter's above the Doge's Palace, and places Eton Chapel on the shores of the Venetian lagoon.

Of this more exaggerated type the Windsor drawings have little to show, but there are many
examples that illustrate the gradual intermingling of fantasy and reality, by which process at a 28, 50, 52
given moment the *veduta esatta* becomes virtually a *capriccio*. Among the strangest are certain more
or less stereotype Venetian views, in which the architectural features are essentially exact, while 60-62
the effect of distance and intervening space is utterly falsified. It may be doubted, however, whether
these interesting but not very pleasing compositions were really conceived in the *capriccio* spirit; and

the question arises whether we are not confronted here, if anywhere in the collection, with the problem of Canaletto's use of the *camera optica*.[35] The problem is difficult and involved; but that Canaletto, like many of his contemporaries, had recourse to this aid can hardly be doubted in view of the evidence available. Zanetti's testimony in this respect is perfectly clear; he complicates the issue, however, in stating that Canaletto demonstrated the proper use and genuine benefit of the camera, by consistently mitigating the distortions it was apt to occasion. If this latter statement were to be taken as literally as the other, one would have to admit the impossibility of detecting it in any particular case, and the problem would cease to have practical significance. It is reasonable to assume, however, despite Zanetti's statement to the contrary, that some distortion of the perspective is likely to remain if the camera is used, and that such distortion affords the only visible evidence, be it in the case of Canaletto or any other artist. The drawings in question can only be regarded as anomalous, whether by caprice or by the application of a scientific aid, whether by virtue of the oddity of their conception, or by the indifference they display to an obvious need for correction. With this the whole question of the *camera optica*, so far as the present collection is concerned, becomes of subordinate interest. Perhaps the most convincing suggestion that has been made so far is that of Hadeln, who cited as possible examples of its use certain outline sketches at Berlin and elsewhere,[36] more or less diagrammatic in style, and bearing annotations which go some way to support his contention.

One further type of drawing, lacking in the Windsor series, should at least be mentioned, in order that these introductory remarks on a collection so nearly complete in itself may cover the subject in its entirety. It would be strange if an artist so skilful in painting figures had not left some mark as a figure draughtsman. Only very few figure drawings by Canaletto have in fact come to light, a number so small in relation to what must once have existed, that one can only assume that they were regarded as practically valueless after use, and that those that have survived owe their preservation to mere accident. It may be that most of them shared the fate of the topographical camera studies, which must no doubt also have been numerous; and shared it for the same reason—because they were produced by mechanical aid, and considered, therefore, to be of little interest. The few figure drawings that are known, scattered over various collections,[37] have (with one exception) a quality of outline similar to that in the diagrammatic studies of architectural motives, which, as we have seen, were conjectured by Hadeln to be 'cameragraphs'. This similarity of handling is not improbably due to the same process, and, to save time and trouble, it may well be that Canaletto prepared the *macchiette* that were to animate his pictures with the help of one or other of the available types of instrument, of which there were several, differing in design and purpose.

In any case, the lack of such drawings detracts but little from the value of the Windsor series. For academic reasons they may be missed; æsthetically their absence is scarcely felt. It is much more to be regretted that there is nothing to represent either the opening phase of the youthful artist, or the closing one of a master whose skill remained undiminished to the end of his life. Even so, as was said

---

[35]For general information on the use of the *camera optica* (*camera obscura* or *camera lucida*) as an aid to the draughtsman, see J. Meder, *Die Handzeichnung*, 1919, pp. 477, 550; for more specialized information, H. Fritzsche, *Bernardo Bellotto*, 1936, pp. 180-198, with bibliography. [36]Hadeln, p. 9 (Berlin, No. 5752). A similar sheet was in the Brooke Sale (Christie's, 20 May, 1921, No. 7); another is in the Boymans Museum (Koenigs Collection). A drawing, formerly in the Liphart Collection (Mensing Sale, Amsterdam, 26 October, 1937, No. 38), which connects with a washed drawing at Frankfurt, is perhaps also of this type. Hadeln's opinion, incidentally, is opposed by H. Fritzsche, *Graphische Künste, Mittlg.*, 1930, p. 18. [37]The most notable of the figure drawings are those in the Witt Collection and at Berlin (Hadeln, plates 60-63). A very early example is in the Ashmolean Museum (see above, p. 23) on the reverse of a view of the Rialto Bridge which served for a picture painted in 1725 for Stefano Conti of Lucca. See *Burlington Magazine*, xlix, p. 311, and xlii, p. 284. A similar sheet to Sir Robert Witt's is in the Metropolitan Museum, New York.

FIG. 7. CANALETTO: VENETIAN CAPRICCIO: THE PIAZZETTA WITH THE BRONZE HORSES FROM ST. MARK'S (WINDSOR CASTLE)

at the outset, it is a rich and representative collection, far beyond any other of Canaletto's work, and indeed there is little to compare with it even of other artists. Hadeln's remark that 'this truly Royal collection' is the 'Alpha and Omega of our knowledge of Canaletto as a draughtsman' is as true in substance as it is striking in phrase. Let us, then, proceed to examine it in detail, with the care and attention it deserves.

CATALOGUE

List of Bibliographical Abbreviations

[COLLINS BAKER.] *Catalogue of the Principal Pictures in the Royal Collection at Windsor Castle.* By C. H. Collins Baker, London, 1937.

[FRITZSCHE.] *Bernardo Bellotto genannt Canaletto.* By H. A. Fritzsche. Burg b.M., 1936.

[HADELN.] *The Drawings of Antonio Canal called Canaletto.* By Detlev, Baron von Hadeln. Translated by Campbell Dodgson. London, 1929.

[LORENZETTI.] *Venezia e il suo Estuario.* By G. Lorenzetti. Venice, s.a.

[PALLUCCHINI-GUARNATI.] *Le Acqueforti del Canaletto.* By R. Pallucchini and G. F. Guarnati. Venice (1945).

[POPHAM.] *Italian Drawings exhibited at the Royal Academy, Burlington House, London, 1930.* By A. E. Popham. Oxford, 1937.

[DE VESME.] *Le Peintre-Graveur Italien.* By Alexandre de Vesme. Milan, 1906.

NOTE: THE ABBREVIATIONS Q, R, AND M STAND FOR QUILL PEN, REED PEN, AND METAL PEN RESPECTIVELY

(1—6)

These drawings connect with six large pictures of more or less uniform size, four upright in shape and two oblong, which certainly form a set, and are probably the earliest examples of Canaletto's work acquired by Consul Smith, and retained by him for his collection. All are now at Windsor. Their date (though given as between 1735/40 in the catalogue of the Burlington House Exhibition, 1946/47) may be fixed at about 1726/27 on the topographical evidence of No. 4. Unlike the two oblong drawings, which were almost certainly from nature, the uprights, more especially Nos. 3 and 4, have much the appearance of being drawn from memory, simply as preliminary essays or rough indications of the projected pictures. See above, p. 25. Neither in the present group nor the following, does pinpointing occur, a fact which is consistent with their summary execution. See above, p. 23.

1. VENICE: THE PROCURATIE VECCHIE FROM THE PIAZZETTA (7444). Plate 5.

Pen (QR) in black/brown ink over pencil (traces); $9\frac{3}{16} \times 7\frac{1}{8}$ in. (233 × 188 mm.). Ink lines drawn with the ruler occur in the frontage of the Procuratie.

The drawing corresponds fairly closely with a Windsor picture (Burlington House Exhib., 1946/47, No. 445), in which, however, the angle of the Campanile on the extreme L. seems to have been painted out, while prominent figures have been introduced in the L. foreground. It shows, moreover, two of the three flagstaffs on the Piazza in front of the Basilica, both in a somewhat arbitrary position and moved to the L. for reasons of pictorial effect. The lighting is the same as in the drawing.

2. VENICE: THE PIAZZETTA WITH THE TORRE DELL' OROLOGIO (7443). Plate 1.

Pen (QR) in brown/brownish-black ink over pencil (traces); $9\frac{3}{16} \times 7\frac{1}{16}$ in. (234 × 180 mm.). Some ruled ink lines occur in the foreshortened façade of the Libreria. There is a ruled pencil line along the lower margin.

Exhibited at Burlington House, 1930, No. 836; repr. by Popham, plate CCLXVIIIA, No. 321. Though rather less close in correspondence than the preceding, the drawing certainly connects with a picture at Windsor (Burlington House Exhib., 1946/47, No. 450). This shows the same effect of lighting, and the column of S. Teodoro is again used to frame the composition on the extreme R. But the flagstaffs, omitted from the drawing, are prominently seen, while the clock-tower and adjacent buildings appear nearer to the spectator. The perspective of the Libreria recedes even more steeply, and the dramatic effect is increased by the cornice cutting diagonally across the Campanile.

3. VENICE: S. MARIA DELLA SALUTE FROM THE PIAZZETTA (7445). Plate 4.

Pen (Q) in brown ink over pencil (freehand and ruled); $9\frac{3}{16} \times 7\frac{1}{8}$ in. (233 × 182 mm.).

The extraordinarily capricious placing in this drawing of the column supporting the lion of St. Mark is one of the main reasons for considering Nos. 1-4 to have been drawn from memory. The proportions and architectural details of the Libreria, moreover, show a lack of exactitude which would be hard to reconcile even with a hasty study from nature. The drawing, while differing considerably, is surely connected with the Windsor picture, Fig. 2 (Collins Baker, p. 37; Burlington House Exhib., 1946/47, No. 454). Here the column of S. Teodoro appears on the R., while that of the lion is omitted; the church bulks larger in the centre distance. For a related picture, lent from the collection of Major John Mills to the Magnasco Society in 1929, see *Burlington Magazine*, Vol. LV, plate 47A. The column of S. Teodoro is here placed even more to the R., and does not overlap the first window of the Libreria. The picture in New York, referred to by Collins Baker, differs essentially by the inclusion of the distant Fonteghetto della Farina, on which see below, No. 48.

4. VENICE: THE ANGLE OF THE DOGE'S PALACE WITH S. GIORGIO MAGGIORE BEYOND (7446). Fig. 8.

Pen (QR) in light brown/brownish-black ink over pencil (traces); $9\frac{3}{16} \times 7$ in. (233 × 177 mm.).

According to the researches of F. Mauroner, the cusp of the campanile of S. Giorgio was modified from its original straight-lined contour to one of onion shape in the course of building operations commenced in June, 1726 (a date confirmed in the diary of Pietro Gradenigo), and completed in 1728. In February, 1774, the tower collapsed, and was

FIG. 8. VENICE: THE ANGLE OF THE DOGE'S PALACE (CAT. NO. 4)

subsequently rebuilt (1791) in its present-day form, which reverted to the original straight-lined cusp. It is on the above evidence that the drawing under consideration may securely be dated, along with its companions, at about 1726/27. (For the same reason a date after 1728 imposes itself on No. 12, also Nos. 8, 35, etc., all of which show the modified cusp.) A drawing in the Ashmolean Museum (repr. *Old Master Drawings*, Vol. XIII, 1938, plate 12), is closely related to No. 4, and shows an equally broad, though less untidy treatment. It is certainly of the same date, and such obviously 'incorrect' features as the placing of the windows, and of the roundels above them, confirm the impression of a sketch from memory, as in the case of the Windsor sheet. A directly related picture is at Windsor (Collins Baker, p. 38, plate 9; Burlington House Exhib., 1946/47, No. 441); and as with preceding composition, another version from the collection of Major John Mills was lent to the Magnasco Society Exhibition of 1929 (No. 16).

5. VENICE: PIAZZA DI S. MARCO, FACING THE BASILICA (7429). Plate 2.

Pen (Q) in grey/black ink; $7\frac{1}{16} \times 9\frac{1}{4}$ in. (180 × 234 mm.). There are no traces of pencil. The ruler was used for drawing the L. outline of the Campanile, the steeply receding pavement line on R., and the flagstaffs.

The Windsor picture (Collins Baker, p. 39, plate 10; Burlington House Exhib., 1946/47, No. 443), though it shows more foreground and the buildings in it bulk rather larger, is essentially the same; it corresponds, for instance, closely in the heavy shadow on R. passing diagonally across the base of the Campanile, producing thus a strong contrast to the sunlit front of the Doge's Palace which is seen in the distance between the tower and the Procuratie.

6. VENICE: PIAZZA DI S. MARCO, FACING THE CHURCH OF S. GEMINIANO (7434). Plate 3.

Pen (QR) in grey/black ink; $7\frac{1}{16} \times 9\frac{3}{8}$ in. (180 × 233 mm.). There are no traces of pencil. A number of ruled lines occur in the foreshortened façade of the Procuratie.

This relates to the Windsor picture, Fig. 3 (Collins Baker, p. 37; Burlington House Exhib., 1946/47, No. 442). This is modified to the extent of including the Loggetta and base of the Campanile on L., and also one of the flagstaffs on R. The concentration of shadow on L. and the inclusion (though at a greater distance) of the temporary platform on R., are similar. In the picture the cusp of S. Moisè does not project so high.

(7—11)

On the evidence of a drawing at Darmstadt closely resembling No. 10, this whole group of brilliantly free and atmospheric sketches may reliably be dated at about 1729. All have the convincing appearance of being drawn in the open (see above, p. 25); though in some cases compositional correspondence may be noted with known pictures, it is probable that all were made quite independently, without any specific intention of after-use. There are no visible traces of pin-pointing (see above, p. 23), but only once (No. 8) does preliminary pencil work seem to have been dispensed with. Ruled lines are not infrequent. Not only in shape and scale are the drawings more or less alike; their actual measurements show a fairly close correspondence, and, allowing for some slight clipping of the margins, they may reasonably be assumed to have been originally identical.

7. VENICE: THE MOLO WITH THE BUCINTORO AT ANCHOR (7451). Plate 6.

Pen (QR) in brown/black ink; $8\frac{5}{8} \times 12\frac{1}{2}$ in. (211 × 318 mm.) Various auxiliary verticals and a horizon-line are drawn with pencil, but there seems to be no free-hand pencil-work.

This view from the Bacino with the Bucintoro moored at the quai-side was drawn no doubt on Ascension Day before the embarking of the Doge to perform the annual ceremony of the *Sposalizio dal Mar*, that is the symbolic marriage of Venice to the Adriatic. There are a number of similar paintings (including the Bucintoro), of which one is at Windsor (Collins Baker, p. 41; Burlington House Exhib., 1946/47, No. 446; repr. *Burl. Mag.*, XXIII, p. 271). This was engraved by Visentini in *Prospectus Magni Canalis*, 1735, Plate XIV. It differs essentially, however, as do pictures in the Hermitage, the Aldo Crespi Collection, and elsewhere, in having in the L. foreground the characteristic motive of boatmen striving to avoid a collision; in similar views, such as that of the Wallace Collection and the Seely Sale (Christie's, 28 June, 1928, No. 161), where the said motive does not occur, the Bucintoro is absent; in other words, the scene is not that of the Sposalizio ceremony. A picture at Dulwich agrees with the drawing in that the one motive is absent and the other present, but its execution is surely of later date.

8. VENICE: THE PIAZZETTA, FACING S. GIORGIO MAGGIORE (7441). Plate 9.

Pen (QR) in brown/brownish-black ink; $8\frac{3}{8} \times 12\frac{7}{16}$ in. (212 × 317 mm.). There are no traces of pencil work. Ruled ink lines occur on L.

Magnasco Society Exhib., 1929, No. 21; Burlington House, 1930, No. 823 (repr. by Popham, plate CCLXVII, B). The onion-shaped cusp of S. Giorgio (see above, p. 29) suggests a date after 1728, and this is confirmed by the dated drawing of 1729 inscribed *Veduta della Piaza Verso il*

Mar, which was sold with the Bateson Collection (Sotheby, 23 April, 1929, No. 16; repr. *Burl. Mag.* XLIX, p. 314). Somewhat similar (but not including the Libreria on R.) is the composition of Canaletto's etching entitled *la Piera del Bando V.* (Pallucchini and Guarnati, No. 17). The famous stone at the Southern angle of the façade of St. Mark's, from which the *Comandador* proclaimed the decrees of State, appears more prominently in the etching No. 15.

9. VENICE: THE ZECCA AND ADJACENT BUILDINGS (7460). Plate 7.

Pen (QR) in black/brownish-grey ink over pencil (freehand); 7 11/16 × 12 in. (195×305 mm.). There are many ink lines drawn with the ruler.

This view from the Bacino is of particular interest since it shows more clearly than others of the same type the massive frontage of the Granai (i.e., the State Granaries) which were formerly situated adjacent to the Zecca. The building was demolished in Napoleonic times to make way for what is to-day the Giardinetto Reale. Of the many pictures by Canaletto showing roughly this view, nearly all render the quay-side and Granai in steeper perspective. This applies also to the brilliantly free and rapid sketch inscribed *Veduta della pescharie* (referring to the *old* fish-market), which is related to two early drawings (one dated 1729), formerly in the Bateson Collection, and belongs to the Pennsylvania Academy at Philadelphia. See O. Benesch, *Venetian Drawings . . . in America*, 1947, plate 48. On the Fonteghetto della Farina, beyond the Granai, and the prominent rectangular tower, another lost landmark, here seen in the far distance on L., see below, No. 48.

10. VENICE: RIVA DEGLI SCHIAVONI (7452). Plate 8.

Pen (Q) in brownish-black/brown ink over pencil (freehand and ruled). 7 11/16 × 12 3/16 in. (196×309 mm.). There are many ruled ink lines.

There is a closely related drawing in the Darmstadt Museum, showing the same view within a double ruled border-line, inscribed in the upper margin in Canaletto's hand *Veduta Versso Castello cioe della piacetta*, and in the lower *Marzo 1729 Venetia.* Hadeln's reproduction (Plate 7) omits these inscriptions, but the complete drawing is rendered in *Stift und Feder*, 1930, 39 (Darmstadt 231). The handling is very similar, but slightly rougher; there are various minor modifications, such as the omission of the temporary boarded structure near the Ponte della Paglia. Both drawings are certainly original. The National Gallery picture, No. 940, though not directly related, shares with the drawing the rather unusual feature of being viewed from a point from which the lion column appears to L. of the angle of the Doge's Palace. With the column to R. of it, the view was one of the most frequently repeated.

11. VENICE: VIEW ALONG THE RIVA DEGLI SCHIAVONI, FACING TOWARDS S. MARCO (7457). Fig. 9.

Pen (Q) in brown ink over pencil (freehand and ruled); 8 3/8 × 12 1/2 in. (213×318 mm.). There is some illegible writing in pencil on the broad house-front on R.

The view is the same as No. 23, and the present rapid sketch may possibly have been used for that more detailed drawing, although another, at Darmstadt (AE 2198), is perhaps closer to it. Hadeln (p. 20) connects it with a picture in the Vienna Gallery. The Soane Museum has a fine painted version which includes S. Giorgio on the extreme L.; see also No. 31 of the Castiglioni Sale (Mensing, 1925).

FIG. 9. VENICE: THE RIVA DEGLI SCHIAVONI, FACING S. MARCO (CAT. NO. 11)

12. VENICE: THE ANGLE OF THE DOGE'S PALACE WITH S. GIORGIO MAGGIORE BEYOND (7442). Plate 23.

Pen (Q) in brown ink over pencil (freehand and ruled) and much pin-pointing; 10 5/8 × 6 3/8 in. (270×188 mm.). There is a ruled ink line, running horizontally, near the base of the column, and another ruled line, also more or less horizontal but drawn in red chalk, at the lower level of the capital surmounting the corner pillar of the palace loggia. A *pentimento* is noticeable to L. of the church tower, where the preliminary indications in pencil show that the masts were originally intended to rise to a greater height.

The view is the same as in No. 4, but the onion-shaped cusp of S. Giorgio shows that the drawing is of later date (see above, p.29). Like a drawing at Oxford, resembling No. 4 in breadth of handling, the present view shows three windows in the frontage of the Doge's Palace and the corner of the centre balcony. On the reverse are two studies of barges or *bragozzi*, drawn in ink over pencil, but the execution is feeble and seems not to be by Canaletto.

13. VENICE: CANALE DI S. CHIARA (7476). Plate 10.

Pen (Q) in black/dark brown ink over pencil (ruled) and pin-pointing; 7 7/16 × 10 11/16 in. (199×271 mm.).

The view is roughly to the South, that is towards the Fondamenta della Croce. The roof of the church of S. Croce is seen projecting above the encircling wall of the convent of Corpus Domini on the L. bank. The drawing relates directly to a picture (Fig. 5) formerly the property of Sir Robert Grenville Harvey, of Langley Park, which is one of a series of twenty Venetian views, eleven of which were engraved either in the first, second or third parts of Antonio Visentini's *Urbis Venetiarum Prospectus Celebriores*, 1735/42. The whole series was exhibited in the Ashmolean Museum in 1936, and is now deposited at Birmingham.

14. VENICE: THE LOWER REACHES OF THE CANALE DI S. CHIARA (7473). Fig. 10.

Pen (Q) in brownish-black/brown ink over pencil (freehand and ruled) and pin-pointing; 10 11/16 × 14 13/16 in. (270×376 mm.). Some ink lines drawn with the ruler occur.

The view should be compared with Nos. 13 and 15. Hadeln's description of it as the Rio di S. Sebastiano has no foundation in fact. The church of S. Croce is seen in the distance on L. with the Tolentini projecting above the house to R. of it. A very similar composition (but with different figures) was engraved by Visentini as plate II/1

FIG. 10. VENICE: CANALE DI S. CHIARA (CAT. NO. 14)

of his *Urbis Venetiarum Prospectus Celebriores* of 1742; another such picture, of good quality, is in the Wallace Collection. Both show the motive that occurs also in the drawing of a *burchiello* (i.e., passenger barge) being towed by a *barca* in the middle distance.

In the R. foreground is a house with an oval sign attached to a balcony. Though often described as the British Consulate, and, indeed, sometimes (which is equally wrong), as the house of Consul Smith (see above, p. 14), it was in fact at one time the house of the British Secretary Resident. A view along the canal from near S. Croce, lent by Leo Goldschmied to the 1930 exhibition at Burlington House (No. 793), has an inscription on the reverse giving the date of the picture as 'about 1730', and stating that a gentleman just alighted from a gondola in front of the house, was Colonel Elizaeus Burgess, who was Resident in 1719/22 and 1728/36. A similar picture is at Windsor (Collins Baker, p. 30). (See also *Burlington Magazine*, Vol. LX (1932), p. 204.)

15. VENICE: THE CONFLUENCE OF THE GRAND AND S. CHIARA CANALS (7489). Fig. 11.

Pen (Q) in dark/light brown ink; $6\frac{7}{8}\times9\frac{9}{16}$ in. (175×242 mm.). There is no pencil work or pin-pointing.

The view is similar to the two preceding, but is from a point nearer to S. Croce. The paper being rather thin, the same view, drawn to a rather larger scale on the reverse, shows through to the front, as may even be seen in the reproduction. The drawing is also dated on the reverse *16 luglio 1734* (almost certainly 1734, not 1737 nor 1739, though the last numeral is perhaps a trifle obscure). In this connexion, see below, No. 37.

FIG. 11. VENICE: THE CONFLUENCE OF THE GRAND AND S. CHIARA CANALS (CAT. NO. 15)

16. VENICE: THE UPPER REACHES OF THE GRAND CANAL, FACING S. CROCE (7472). Plate 25.

Pen (QM) in dark brown/brown ink over pencil (freehand and ruled) and pin-pointing; $10\frac{5}{8}\times14\frac{7}{8}$ in. (269×377 mm.).

The view shows the façade of S. Croce in the R. foreground, with the churches of Corpus Domini, S. Lucia and the Scalzi on the opposite bank. In the distance on the R. bank is the dome of S. Simeone Piccolo (built 1718/38). The site of S. Lucia is that of the present-day railway station. A copy by Bellotto at Darmstadt is listed by Fritzsche (VZ 26). The same view with a similar *burchiello* in the L. foreground was engraved by Visentini as plate II/2 of his *Prospectus Celebriores* of 1742. This corresponds with a picture in the Langley Park series, a poor copy of which was in the 1911 Crespi Sale (No. 66). There are two versions in the National Gallery. No. 2514 again has the *burchiello*, and, like the drawing, shows only a circular window in the façade of the church. No. 1886 is viewed from a point closer to S. Croce, omits the burchiello and churches of the L. bank, and has two narrow windows above the side doors of the church, and a cross surmounting the gable of the roof.

(17-21)

This group, in which No. 16 should perhaps also have been included, comprises a series of views of the Grand Canal, remarkable for their bigness of conception, and a certain dramatic quality which in some is reminiscent of the National Gallery 'Stonemason's Yard'. They show various topographical features of special interest, without, however, enabling one to assign a precise date either to any individual drawing or the series as a whole. The evidence of style makes it probable that they are roughly of the mid-'thirties. With the exception of No. 19, possibly clipped at top or bottom, the sizes are more or less uniform, and correspond with those of No. 16. All were probably drawn from nature. Only No. 20 can be closely connected with a picture.

17. VENICE: THE LOWER REACHES OF THE GRAND CANAL FROM NEAR PALAZZO CORNER (7469). Plate 26.

Pen (QR) in brownish-black/brown ink over pencil (freehand and ruled) and pin-pointing; $10\frac{5}{8}\times14\frac{11}{16}$ in. (270×374 mm.). Ruled ink lines occur in the façade of the palace on R.

Exhibited by the Magnasco Society in 1929, No. 25, and at Burlington House in 1930, No. 820. Reproduced by Popham, plate CCLXV. A copy at Darmstadt is listed by Fritzsche (VZ 23). The following drawing, No. 18, is similar but not so fine. Both, but more especially No. 17, resemble a picture formerly in the collection of King William II of Holland, and now the property of the Counts zu Wied.

18. VENICE: THE LOWER REACHES OF THE GRAND CANAL FROM NEAR PALAZZO CORNER (7470). Plate 27.

Pen (QR) in brownish-black/greyish-brown ink over pencil (ruled) and much pin-pointing; $10\frac{5}{8}\times14\frac{11}{16}$ in. ($270\times$ 374 mm.). Ink lines drawn with the ruler occur in various places.

The drawing resembles No. 17 but has different figures and boats. It also resembles, but again with differences in the figures, the composition engraved by Visentini as plate II/10 of the *Prospectus Celebriores* of 1742. The palace in the R. foreground is the Prefettura of to-day, that is the Palazzo Corner della Cà Grande, not as stated by Hadeln, the Palazzo Corner della Regina (now Monte di Pietà, situated beyond the Rialto on the opposite side of the canal near the Palazzo Pesaro). The distant church tower on L. is that of S. Maria della Carità which collapsed in 1741.

19. VENICE: THE LOWER REACHES OF THE GRAND CANAL, FACING THE BEND (7474). Plate 28.

Pen (QR) in brownish-black/greyish-brown ink over pencil (freehand and ruled) and pin-pointing; $8\frac{5}{8}\times 14\frac{13}{16}$ in. (220×376 mm.). There are ruled ink lines in the façade of the palace in the L. foreground.

A copy of this drawing, presumably by Bellotto, was in the Geiger Sale of 1920 (Sotheby, 7/10 Dec., No. 52; from the Darmstadt and Goldschmidt Collections). The view shows the unfinished Palazzo Rezzonico in the distance, centre, and the Palazzo Quirini in the L. foreground. The open space in the R. foreground is what is popularly known as the 'Stonemason's Yard', the building flanking it being in exact correspondence with the details of the famous picture in the National Gallery (cp. Fig. 4). The scene is viewed from in front of the Scuola della Carità, now reconstructed, as is the church adjoining it, to form the Accademia di Belle Arti.

20. VENICE: THE BEND IN THE LOWER REACHES OF THE GRAND CANAL (7468). Plate 29.

Pen (Q) in brownish-black/brown ink over pencil (freehand and ruled) and pin-pointing; $10\frac{11}{16}\times 14\frac{3}{4}$ in. (272×375 mm.).

A copy by Bellotto, at Darmstadt, is listed by Fritzsche (VZ 25). There is a picture in the Lyons Museum which corresponds closely, even with the boats and figures. As in No. 19, the Palazzo Rezzonico is seen (in L. foreground) with its temporary roof, before a further storey was added and the building completed in 1745. Adjoining it are the Giustinian and Foscari palaces, followed, *in volta di canal*, by the Palazzo Balbi-Guggenheim. It is flanked on L. and R. by the belfries of the Frari and S. Tomà. The distant palace on the R. is the Moro-Lin; that of which only the angle is seen in the R. foreground is the Malipiero. The open space adjoining it is the Campo S. Samuele; between it and the Palazzo Moro-Lin is the site of the Palazzo Grassi-Stucky, but this building (by Giorgio Massari) had not yet been erected.

21. VENICE: THE LOWER MIDDLE REACHES OF THE GRAND CANAL, FACING THE RIALTO (7471). Plate 30.

Pen (QR) in dark brown ink over pencil (freehand and ruled) and pin-pointing; $10\frac{5}{8}\times 14\frac{7}{8}$ in. (270×377 mm.). The ruler was probably used for some of the line-work in ink.

Hadeln is wrong in calling the palace in the R. foreground the Palazzo Mocenigo. This in fact stands further back, and it is the Palazzo Corner-Spinelli that is represented. Beyond it, the Palazzo Grimani bulks large in the R. middle distance, with the Palazzo Coccina-Tiepolo-Papadopoli, easily recognizable by the obelisks surmounting its façade, nearly opposite. One end of the Rialto bridge is visible in the distance, centre.

22. VENICE: THE CANALE DI S. MARCO WITH THE BUCINTORO AT ANCHOR (7453). Plate 24.

Pen (QM) in brownish-black/brown ink over pencil (freehand and ruled) and much pin-pointing; $10\frac{9}{16}\times 14\frac{13}{16}$ in. (268×376 mm.). There is a ruled pencil horizon-line extending across the page from margin to margin. The outline of the larger dome of the Salute may have been drawn with the compasses.

The composition is of a standard type, but the drawing seems not to be directly related to any known picture. No. 4453 of the National Gallery is similar, but viewed from a greater distance. The Bucintoro being moored at the Molo in readiness for the Doge's embarkation, it is probable that the scene connects with the ceremony of the Sensa.

23. VENICE: VIEW ALONG THE RIVA DEGLI SCHIAVONI, FACING TOWARDS S. MARCO (7455). Plate 32.

Pen (QM) in black ink over pencil (freehand and ruled) and pin-pointing; $8\frac{1}{16}\times 14\frac{3}{16}$ in. (205×376 mm.). Certain lines in the foreground seem to have been drawn with the aid of the ruler.

The view which embraces a panorama from S. Giorgio to S. Marco and the buildings adjacent to it, and includes in the foreground the houses of the waterfront of the Riva, resembles that represented in No. 11, but according to Hadeln the drawing was worked up from AE 2198 at Darmstadt. A somewhat similar picture is in the Soane Museum; another was in the Castiglioni Collection.

24. VENICE: VIEW ACROSS THE BACINO FROM THE RIVA DEGLI SCHIAVONI (7454). Plate 33.

Pen (QM) in brown ink over pencil (freehand and ruled) and pin-pointing; $10\frac{1}{2}\times 14\frac{3}{4}$ in. (268×375 mm.).

Exhibited by the Magnasco Society in 1929 (No. 23). The view resembles Nos. 11 and 23 but is from nearer the Molo. The curve of the waterfront of the Riva seems to be much exaggerated in the foreground. A similar effect occurs in the British Museum drawing 1910. 2.12.19, one of the Mocenigo series engraved by Brustolon.

25. VENICE: THE LIBRERIA AND CAMPANILE FROM THE PIAZZETTA (7437). Plate 12.

Pen (QM) in black/brownish-black ink over pencil (freehand and ruled) and much pin-pointing; $10\frac{5}{8}\times 14\frac{3}{4}$ in. (270×375 mm.).

A detail worth noting is that the artist has omitted to work over with the pen some of the flying birds sketched in with pencil. In this connexion, see above, p. 22. The Windsor picture of 1743 (Collins Baker, p. 44; Burlington House Exhib., 1946/47, No. 453) is different in perspective and includes the lion column. No. 939 in the National Gallery is more nearly the same view, and omits the column, but there is certainly no direct connexion. No. 56 of the Greffulhe Sale (Sotheby, 22 July, 1937), though of the same standard type, differs in lighting.

26. VENICE: THE FAÇADE OF S. MARCO AND THE DOGE'S PALACE (7428). Plate 14.

Pen (QM) in black/greyish-brown ink over pencil (freehand and ruled) and pin-pointing; $10\frac{5}{8}\times 14\frac{9}{16}$ in. (270×376 mm.). The ruler was used for drawing the flagstaffs.

An outline drawing in the British Museum (1910. 2.12.27) shows close correspondence even with the figures. Though considered genuine by Hadeln and reproduced by him (plate 39), it is by no means convincing in quality, and more nearly resembles the Darmstadt Bellottos. Hadeln (p.13) refers to a copy by Bellotto at Darmstadt (AE 2212), but this item does not occur in Fritzsche's lists. A picture, formerly at Castle Howard and now in the National Gallery of Washington, D.C., is similar, but viewed from a more elevated position. The frontage of the buildings is in steeper perspective. No. 60 of the Kilmorey Sale (Sotheby, 3 December, 1924) is another of the same general type. It extends further to the L. and shows other differences; but there are certain analogies among the figures, though not a close correspondence.

27. VENICE: THE TORRE DELL' OROLOGIO AND PIAZZETTA DEI LEONCINI (7425). Plate 11.

Pen (QM) in black/dark brownish-grey ink over pencil (freehand and ruled) and pin-pointing; $10\frac{5}{8} \times 14\frac{7}{8}$ in. (271 × 377 mm.). The use of the ruler is clearly discernible in the flagstaffs and some of the receding pavement lines near the R. lower corner.

A picture in the Ottawa Gallery, formerly in the Farnborough Hall Collection, is essentially of the same type as this drawing; but it omits several of the arches of the Procuratie Vecchie, which appear in the latter. The effect of lighting is the same, and though the figures do not correspond, there are three similar stalls with sun-shades near the angle of St. Mark's.

FIG. 12. S. MARCO IN FANCIFUL SETTING (CAT. NO. 28)

28. VENETIAN CAPRICCIO: S. MARCO IN FANCIFUL SETTING (7432). Fig. 12.

Pen (QM) in black/dark brown ink over pencil (freehand and ruled) and pin-pointing; $10\frac{5}{8} \times 14\frac{3}{4}$ in. (270 × 375 mm.).

The North angle of the façade of St. Mark's is essentially accurate in rendering (cp. No. 27, plate 11), but the lion to the R. of the Portale di S. Alipio is a capricious addition. The general setting is, of course, purely fanciful.

29. VENICE: THE ARSENAL AND PONTE DEL PARADISO (7477). Plate 31.

Pen (QM) in black/brownish-black ink over pencil (freehand and ruled) and pin-pointing; $10\frac{11}{16} \times 14\frac{13}{16}$ in. (271 × 376 mm.).

A copy by Bellotto at Darmstadt, but with different figures, is listed by Fritzsche (VZ 24). Another version, also with different figures and boats, was lent by Max Rosenheim to the Burlington Fine Arts Club in 1911, No. 69, (see below, No. 32). The Arsenal does not occur as frequently as might be expected among the *vedute* of Canaletto and his School. A picture in the Ottawa Gallery, formerly in the Bertram Hardy Collection, shows the gateway in side view with the old wheeled bridge (represented in the centre of the present drawing) on the extreme R. The two compositional types correspond more or less with etchings by Carlevarijs, viz., No. 62 and 63 of his *Fabriche e Vedute*, 1703. Over the door of the chapel of the Madonna dell' Arsenale, on the extreme R. of our drawing, is a minute papal coat-of-arms charged with a mount of three summits, surmounted by a star. It refers, of course, to Alexander VII (Chigi), 1655/67.

30. VENICE: THE NORTH TRANSEPT OF S. MARCO (7430). Plate 15.

Pen (QM) in black/brownish-black ink over pencil (traces) and pin-pointing; $10\frac{11}{16} \times 7\frac{3}{8}$ in. (272 × 188 mm.). Ruled ink lines occur (e.g., the two verticals from which the cross and lamp are suspended). Traces of indentation with the point of the dividers are visible in the small, heavily shaded arch immediately above the *iconostasi*. The remotest of the large arches, and the segment in the L. upper corner are drawn in ink with the aid of the compasses.

Exhibited by the Magnasco Society in 1929 (No. 20). The view is from below the periphery of the Cupola di S. Leonardo into the N. transept of the Basilica, with the entrance to the Cappella di S. Isidoro near the lower L. corner. The actual ceremony or incident represented is problematical. There are two pictures by Canaletto at Windsor, one of which is a view down the aisle of the church (Collins Baker, p. 36; Burlington House Exhib., 1946/47, No. 455), and is described in Smith's inventory as 'Inside of St. Mark's Church on Good Friday'; the other corresponds essentially with the present drawing and is listed as 'Ditto with Innumerable figures by night' (Collins Baker, p. 36; Burlington House Exhib., No. 452). On the face of it, it would seem probable that the descriptions of the two pictures were confused, and that No. 452 of the Exhibition, not No. 455, was the Good Friday scene. In that case it would have been plausible to assume that the sarcophagus beneath a canopy, visible in the distance of the picture and of our drawing which corresponds with it, and represented on a larger scale in the drawing No. 31 (cp. also the Hamburg drawing of 1766, repr. by Hadeln, plate 56), was the *sepolcro santo* which in Roman Catholic churches is erected on Maundy Thursday and remains displayed till the eve of Easter. But ecclesiastical specialists deny that either of the pictures can show the interior of St. Mark's as it would have appeared in Holy Week; and, hard as it is to explain how the idea of Good Friday can have crept into Smith's inventory (whether in relation to the one or other of the two pictures) by error or misinformation, their pronouncement must be accepted. That being so, the sarcophagus cannot be the *sepolcro santo*, and one can only assume that it was in the nature of a reliquary. It has been thought that the scene represented in the drawing, No. 30, might conceivably be the reception of the relics of Doge S. Pietro Orseolo (7 February, 1733), but no confirmation of this is available, and the suggestion remains purely conjectural.

31. VENICE: A SARCOPHAGUS RELIQUARY IN THE NORTH TRANSEPT OF S. MARCO (7431). Plate 16.

Pen (QM) in black/brownish-black ink over pencil (freehand and ruled); $10\frac{5}{8} \times 7\frac{3}{8}$ in. (270 × 188 mm.). A ruled horizon-line, drawn with pencil, extends across the page from margin to margin. There is a ruled ink line just below the lid of the sarcophagus.

The sarcophagus is shown on a small scale in No. 30 and also in the Hamburg drawing of 1766 (repr. Hadeln, plate 56). The pattern on the wall behind the *baldacchino* seems to be vaguely indicated in the Windsor drawing, but not in the other (see the preceding note).

(32-36)

Though not uniform in size, these drawings seem to form a distinct series of views of Venetian churches, a common feature of all being their rather dry and mechanical execution. All make the definite impression of deriving from previously made studies, and not of having been drawn on the spot, that is from nature (see above, p.25). Such connexions as there are with pictures should be considered, therefore, as incidental. Much inferior though they are to the quality of Canaletto's best drawings, it can hardly be doubted that they are all by the Master's hand.

32. VENICE: S. SIMEONE PICCOLO (7467). Fig. 13.
Pen (QM) in black/dark grey ink over pencil (freehand and ruled) and pin-pointing; $8\frac{7}{8} \times 14\frac{11}{16}$ in. (227×375 mm.). The ruler seems to have been used.

A copy by Bellotto, at Darmstadt, is listed by Fritzsche (VZ 29); this shows the portico of the church in a frontal view, and is possibly identical with one of five, alleged to come from the Darmstadt Collection, which have recently

FIG. 13. VENICE: S. SIMEONE PICCOLO (CAT. NO. 32)

been in the trade. The figures and boats show analogies with the Windsor version, but are not identical. Another version, certainly inferior to the Windsor drawing and perhaps also by Bellotto, was lent by Max Rosenheim to the Burlington Fine Arts Club in 1911 (No. 64), and, when in the Rudolf Collection, to the Matthiesen Gallery Exhibition of 1939 (No. 126). The catalogue of the latter points out that, since the steps leading up to the entrance to the church are (as in the Windsor drawing) represented in an unfinished state, the date is probably before 1738, in which year, according to Lorenzetti, the building was completed (see above, No. 16). The picture, No. 1885, of the National Gallery, shows Scalfarotto's church in a similar view, but with finished steps. A washed drawing by Canaletto, now at Detroit, formerly in the Fraser-Tytler Collection (Christie, 21 July, 1924, No. 18), is a *capriccio* using motives of S. Simeone.

33. VENICE: S. PIETRO IN CASTELLO (7485). Fig. 14.
Pen (QM) in black ink over pencil (traces) and pin-pointing; $10\frac{3}{16} \times 14\frac{3}{4}$ in. (234×374 mm.). Some ruled ink lines

FIG. 14. VENICE: S. PIETRO IN CASTELLO (CAT. NO. 33)

occur. The outline of the dome is drawn with the compasses.

There are painted versions of this subject in the National Gallery (No. 1059), and the Gymnasium zum Grauen Kloster in Berlin (Photo Alinari, No. 45511). Both differ from the drawing in regard to accessories, and show considerably more of the bridge on R.

34. VENICE: IL REDENTORE (7484). Fig. 15.
Pen (QM) in black/brownish-black ink over pencil (traces) and much pin-pointing; $10\frac{5}{8} \times 14\frac{11}{16}$ in. (268×373 mm.)

A picture, formerly the property of the late Sir George Leon and included in the 1930 Canaletto Exhibition at the Savile Gallery, gives a somewhat similar frontal view of the church from the canal of the Giudecca, but from a point less remote. The church of S. Giacomo, now demolished, which stood to the W. of the Redentore, is made to appear considerably closer to it than was really the case. A drawing in the Fogg Art Museum, Cambridge, Mass. (Sachs-Mongan, *Catalogue*, No. 313, Fig. 153) shows the Redentore in fanciful setting, much as the Detroit drawing mentioned under No. 32 shows S. Simeone Piccolo.

35. VENICE: S. GIORGIO MAGGIORE (7482). Fig. 16.
Pen (QM) in black and brown/brownish-black ink over pencil (freehand and ruled) and much pin-pointing; $10\frac{9}{16} \times 14\frac{13}{16}$ in. (268×377 mm.). Some ruled ink lines occur

FIG. 15. VENICE: IL REDENTORE (CAT. NO. 34)

FIG. 16. VENICE: S. GIORGIO MAGGIORE (CAT. NO. 35)

(e.g., the mast and flagstaff to L. and R. respectively). The dome of the church was partly drawn with the aid of the compasses.

The view, which contains obvious elements of caprice, is doubtless intended to be from the Canale della Giudecca at its confluence with the Canale di S. Marco, and with the Punta della Dogana appearing in the L. foreground. Being so, however, S. Giorgio is made to seem far too close, as is the distant church of La Pietà on the Riva degli Schiavoni (extreme L. of drawing). If the date of Massari's reconstruction of the latter is correctly given by Lorenzetti (1745), it would seem that the drawing must have been carried out shortly before Canaletto's departure for England, if not in the interval between his two English periods. The point, however, is somewhat obscure. On the onion-shaped cusp of S. Giorgio, see the note to No. 4. In the Windsor picture (Collins Baker, p. 38) the church is placed in a fanciful setting and the belfry capriciously omitted. The drawing No. 47 of the Oppenheimer Sale (Christie's, 10 July, 1936) was another, more exaggerated *capriccio* on the theme of S. Giorgio.

36. VENICE: S. FRANCESCO DELLA VIGNA (7494). Fig. 17.
Pen (QM) in black ink over pencil (freehand and ruled) and pin-pointing; $10\frac{5}{8} \times 14\frac{7}{8}$ in. (273 × 377 mm.).

A painting in the Langley Park series (see above, p. 31) is somewhat similar to the drawing without corresponding with it minutely. It differs essentially only in that on R. the house adjoining the church projects further, and therefore overlaps the niche to R. of the doorway. The figures show considerable analogies. In the drawing only the first two words of the inscription below the pediment are legible; in the Langley Park picture the last word is covered. The full inscription DEO VTRIVSQE TEMPLI ÆDIFICATORI, AC REPARATORI is plainly visible in a signed and dated picture of 1744 that belonged to the late Sir George Leon. In this latter the setting is fanciful, and the church is viewed at closer range. Somewhat similar to the drawing is the view represented in a picture of the Leo Goldschmied Collection, Milan, which was attributed by Delogù to Visentini and Zuccarelli (*Pittori Veneti Minori*, 1930, pl. 89), and by Ojetti to Zuccarelli alone (*Il Settecento Italiano*, 1932, Vol. I, pl. CII, No. 156). Here no houses are visible on the R., and the façade of the church is surmounted by five statues.

FIG. 17. VENICE: S. FRANCESCO DELLA VIGNA (CAT. NO. 36)

37. VENICE: S. GEREMIA AND THE CANNAREGIO (7475). Fig. 18.
Pen (Q) in brownish-black ink over pencil (freehand and ruled) and pin-pointing; $7\frac{3}{8} \times 10\frac{11}{16}$ in. (188 × 270 mm.).

A copy was sold as lot 7 of the Drouot Sale of 23 December, 1935. The view showing the church of S. Geremia and its belfry on the L., adjoining the latter the Palazzo Labia, the distant buildings of the Ghetto Vecchio and the Ponte di Cannaregio in centre, and on the extreme R. the Palazzo Querini detti Papozze, constitutes a standard type, of which many versions exist. One is at Windsor (Collins Baker, p. 32) and was engraved by Visentini as plate X of his *Prospectus Magni Canalis*, 1735. There is no correspondence with the drawing in regard to the figures and boats. No. 1058 of the National Gallery, on the other hand, is not only viewed from the identical spot, but shows far-reaching analogies in its accessories.

FIG. 18. VENICE: S. GEREMIA AND THE CANNAREGIO (CAT. NO. 37)

According to a note inscribed on the mount, an inscription *16 Luglio 1734* occurs on the back of the drawing. Unlike No. 15, No. 37 shows no trace of this from the front, and it is not impossible that a confusion has occurred. It is no longer possible to verify the point since the drawing (like all the other Canalettos at Windsor) is firmly pasted down, and it would involve soaking to lift it. Though the date is the same as that occurring on No. 15, it should be noted that the latter has *luglio* and not *Luglio*. The proximity of the two sites represented might be taken as evidence that the two drawings were in fact executed on the same day, and that the note on the mount recording the date is exact.

FIG. 19. VENICE: CAMPO S. MARIA FORMOSA (CAT. NO. 38)

38. VENICE: CAMPO S. MARIA FORMOSA (7478). Fig. 19.

Pen (Q) in brown ink over pencil (freehand and ruled) and pin-pointing; $10\frac{11}{16} \times 14\frac{7}{8}$ in. (271×377 mm.). Some ruled ink lines occur in the pavement. The outline of the dome seems to have been drawn with the aid of compasses.

The drawing closely resembles No. 39; see the following note.

39. VENICE: CAMPO S. MARIA FORMOSA (7479). Fig. 20.

Pen (M) in black/grey ink over pencil (freehand and ruled) and much pin-pointing; $10\frac{5}{8} \times 14\frac{13}{16}$ in. (270×376 mm.).

Both Hadeln and Fritzsche assert that a copy by Bellotto of No. 39 is at Darmstadt; but in fact this copy (AE 2210; VZ 30) is after No. 38, which it follows closely even in the figures. It is reproduced by Fritzsche, plate 6, facing p. 9. Its handling is noticeably weaker than that of either of the two Windsor drawings; Fritzsche's suggestion that the figures and inscription *Sta Maria Formosa* are by Canaletto himself is unconvincing. The view is reminiscent of plate 31 of Carlevarijs' *Fabriche e Vedute*, 1703. The same view again, but with independent figures, was engraved by Visentini as plate III/VIII of his *Prospectus Celebriores* of 1742. A picture, once in the Fonthill Collection and sold at Christie's on 9 December, 1936 (lot 66), corresponds closely with this engraving.

FIG. 20. VENICE: CAMPO S. MARIA FORMOSA (CAT. NO. 39)

40. VENICE: SS. GIOVANNI E PAOLO AND THE SCUOLA DI S. MARCO (7481). Fig. 21.

Pen (QM) in black/brownish-black ink over pencil (traces) and much pin-pointing; $10\frac{9}{16} \times 14\frac{7}{8}$ in. (269×378 mm.). The arch of the Ponte del Cavallo is incised with the point of the dividers.

A drawing by Bellotto at Darmstadt is signed and dated 8 December, 1740. Though described by Fritzsche (VZ 37; repr. Hadeln, plate 65) as a copy of the Windsor drawing, it is in fact a free rendering of the same scene, and by no means necessarily based on the Windsor version. It extends the scene considerably at both sides, and has more foreground and different figures. The penwork is rather coarse and untidy. But the rendering, for instance, of Verocchio's statue is not so inadequate as to suggest that it was copied from the rather feeble passage in the Windsor drawing. A painting from the collection of Princess Paly, sold at Christie's on 21 June, 1929, corresponds exactly with the Darmstadt drawing. Fine versions of the scene by Canaletto are those at Dresden and Montreal (the latter of 1725/26, from the Conti and Tatton Collections). Both were viewed at closer range than the Windsor drawing. Another version was in the Dudley Sale of 1892 (No. 51).

FIG. 21. VENICE: SS. GIOVANNI E PAOLO (CAT. NO. 40)

41. VENICE: CAMPO S. STEFANO (MOROSINI) (7480). Fig. 22.

Pen (QM) in brown/brownish-black ink over pencil (freehand and ruled) and pin-pointing; $10\frac{11}{16} \times 14\frac{13}{16}$ in. (271×375 mm.). Some ruled ink lines occur.

A copy by Bellotto at Darmstadt is listed by Fritzsche (VZ 57). The same view, but with different figures, was engraved as plate III/VII of Visentini's *Prospectus Celebriores* of 1742 (repr. by Lorenzetti, p. 461). The view is to the South with the church of S. Stefano in the spectator's back. The rear of the Palazzo Franchetti and the church of S. Vidal appear in the distance on R.

42. VENICE: THE PROCURATIE NUOVE FROM THE PIAZZETTA DEI LEONCINI (7423). Plate 13.

Pen (QM) in black ink over pencil (freehand and ruled) and (?) pin-pointing; $7\frac{1}{2} \times 10\frac{3}{4}$ in. (190×274 mm.). The flagstaff and receding pavement lines on R. are drawn with the pen and ruler.

A similar drawing by Bellotto, formerly in the Boehler and Koenigs Collections, now in the Boymans Museum at

FIG. 22. VENICE: CAMPO S. STEFANO (CAT. NO. 41)

Rotterdam, is listed by Fritzsche (VZ 124). A close copy in brown ink, but without the diagonal shading on the buildings, clouds, etc., is at Lockinge, and might also be by Bellotto. A drawing in pen and wash at Chantilly (repr. Uzanne, *Les deux Canaletto*, 1906, p. 73) shows a similar view but, in upright format, from a point slightly more to the South, thus including the foreshortened frontage of the Procuratie Vecchie. More closely related is the etching De Vesme 22 (Pallucchini and Guarnati 16), which in its second state is inscribed *le Procuratie nioue e S. Ziminiano V.* This is from a point somewhat nearer to the Piazza and shows on L. the projecting angle of the *terrazza* and the Arco di S. Alipio, but not, as in the drawing, the three lateral arches. It includes, moreover, the centre flagstaff on the Piazza.

(43-51)

Here are grouped together nine small drawings, for all of which, except one, it is possible to confront a version of simpler execution in pure line with a more elaborate rendering in line and wash. The same will apply later in the case of Nos. 97/8, 127/8, etc. No. 45, which lacks its counterpart in the more elaborate technique, is somewhat in the nature of a variant of No. 46, as are No. 18 of No. 17, and again Nos. 93/4 of No. 92. Throughout the group the quality is very high. Nos. 50 and 51 lead over from pure topography into the category of the capriccio. *On the priority of the versions in pure line, see above, p. 25.*

43. VENICE: THE LIBRERIA FROM THE MOLO (7439). Plate 17.

Pen (QM) in black/brownish-black ink over pencil (traces) and much pin-pointing; $7\frac{7}{16} \times 10\frac{11}{16}$ in. (188×272 mm.). There are a few ink lines drawn with the ruler.

Exhibited by the Magnasco Society in 1929 (No. 22). The placing of the column supporting the lion of St. Mark shows obvious licence; it appears much too close to the other, which in its turn seems to stand too close to the Libreria. On the Granai, appearing beyond the Zecca, see the note to No. 9. The drawing connects directly with the following item.

44. VENICE: THE LIBRERIA FROM THE MOLO (7440). Plate 18.

Pen (QM) in brownish-grey/black ink with grey wash over preliminary pencil (freehand and ruled) and much pin-pointing; $7\frac{3}{8} \times 10\frac{7}{16}$ in. (188×266 mm.). There are ruled ink lines in the pavement.

Both in the architecture and figures the drawing corresponds minutely with No. 43. A minor deviation of lighting occurs on the steps leading up to the Ponte della Pescheria and the frontage of the Granai. The execution is of exceptional brilliance.

45. VENICE: THE DOGE'S PALACE FROM THE CANALE DI S. MARCO (7448). Fig. 23.

Pen (QM) in brown ink over pencil (freehand and ruled) and (?) a little pin-pointing; $7\frac{5}{16} \times 10\frac{5}{8}$ in. (196×271 mm.). There are some ruled ink lines in the pavement of the Piazzetta.

The composition resembles that of Nos. 46/7, but suggests a rather more distant viewpoint. The South front of the Doge's Palace is obviously made to appear too narrow.

46. VENICE: THE DOGE'S PALACE FROM THE CANALE DI S. MARCO (7450). Plate 19.

Pen (Q) in brown ink over pencil (traces) and pin-pointing; $7\frac{3}{8} \times 10\frac{11}{16}$ in. (188×271 mm.).

This is the direct antecedent of No. 47 and also resembles, but less closely, No. 45.

47. VENICE: THE DOGE'S PALACE FROM THE CANALE DI S. MARCO (7449). Plate 20.

Pen (QM) in brown/brownish-black ink over pencil (freehand and ruled) and pin-pointing; $7\frac{7}{16} \times 10\frac{11}{16}$ in. (189×272 mm.).

This drawing follows No. 46 closely, but the execution is more mechanical and noticeably inferior to that of No. 44. Birds have been added in the sky. Two seated figures on the steps of the Molo, corresponding with similar figures in No. 46, are indicated with pencil, but have not been worked over with the pen. See above, p. 25, and compare Nos. 135 and 136.

48. VENICE: THE FONTEGHETTO DELLA FARINA FROM THE MOLO DI TERRA-NOVA (7464). Plate 34.

Pen (QM) in brownish-black ink over pencil (freehand and ruled) and pin-pointing; $7\frac{1}{2} \times 10\frac{11}{16}$ in. (190×272 mm.).

This is a view of particular topographical interest since it shows the eighteenth-century appearance of the waterfront opposite the Dogana del Mar, which has to-day changed in aspect completely. The building on the extreme R. of the drawing is the Eastern extremity of the frontage of the Granai, which was demolished in Napoleonic times to make place for the Giardinetto Reale (see above, p. 31). The

FIG. 23. VENICE: THE DOGE'S PALACE FROM THE CANALE DI S. MARCO (CAT. NO. 45)

lower building with an arched gateway, in centre, is now the Capitaneria di Porto, with the Palazzo Giustinian-Morosini (Albergo Europa) behind it. It served originally as offices of the Magistrato della Farina, and, in 1756, became the seat of the newly founded Venetian Academy of Painting. See G. Fogolari in *L'Arte*, Vol. XVI (1913), pp. 252-3. On a smaller scale this group of buildings, and the Molo adjoining them, may be seen in plates 7, 17, 32, 33, etc., as well as in a number of paintings by Canaletto (at Grenoble, Washington (from Castle Howard), etc.). A detail of the Fonteghetto from a picture in the Crespi Collection is reproduced by R. Longhi, *Viatico per Cinque Secoli di Pitt. Venez.*, 1946, plate 140. Another feature of special interest is the tall, rectangular tower immediately to the L. of the Fonteghetto. This is not, as has been said, a mere licence of the artist, introduced to break the monotony of the line of buildings between the Abbazzia di S. Gregorio and S. Vio. According to the convincing suggestion of sig. F. Mauroner, it formed part of the now almost completely demolished Palazzo Venier dalla Torresella, which adjoined the Palazzo Venier dei Leoni (Lorenzetti; p. 592). The cognomen, *dalla Torresella*, which later passed to the Dorià who acquired the Palace, derived indeed from this very tower. To this day the Rio delle Torreselle preserves its memory in a corrupted form. See G. Tassini, *Curiosità Veneziane*, ed. 1933, p. 713.

49. VENICE: THE FONTEGHETTO DELLA FARINA FROM THE MOLO DI TERRA-NOVA (7465). Plate 35.

Pen (Q) in brownish-grey ink with grey wash over pencil (freehand) and pin-pointing; $7\frac{7}{16} \times 10\frac{9}{16}$ in. (188 × 269 mm.). There are ruled ink lines in the pavement and elsewhere.

Both the architecture and figures correspond closely with No. 48. On the extreme L. there are certain minor deviations; only a very small portion of the Salute is visible.

50. VENETIAN CAPRICCIO: THE FONTEGHETTO DELLA FARINA IN FANCIFUL SETTING (7462). Fig. 24.

Pen (QR) in brown ink over pencil (freehand and ruled) and pin-pointing; $7\frac{3}{8} \times 10\frac{5}{8}$ in. (188 × 270 mm.). The chevron signature (see above, p. 22) occurs near the centre of the L. margin, but is shaded over and little noticeable.

This is the direct antecedent of No. 51. The building of the Fonteghetto is topographically exact and corresponds closely with Nos. 48/9. The higher building behind it is accurate in the main, but its façade has been embellished with a double order of columns. All the rest is purely fanciful, though the shed and awning on R. have their analogies in the exact view.

FIG. 24. VENETIAN CAPRICCIO: THE FONTEGHETTO DELLA FARINA IN FANCIFUL SETTING (CAT. NO. 50)

51. VENETIAN CAPRICCIO: THE FONTEGHETTO DELLA FARINA IN FANCIFUL SETTING (7463). Plate 36.

Pen (Q) in brownish-black/black ink with grey wash over pencil (traces) and a little pin-pointing; $7\frac{3}{4} \times 10\frac{3}{8}$ in. (197 × 262 mm.). Ruled ink lines occur in the pavement. The chevron signature is plainly indicated near the centre of the L. margin.

This follows No. 50 very closely, but it omits the flying birds and the angle of the Granai on the extreme R.

FIG. 25. VENETIAN CAPRICCIO WITH REMINISCENCES OF THE ZECCA AND PONTE DELLA PESCHERIA (CAT. NO. 52)

52. VENETIAN CAPRICCIO WITH REMINISCENCES OF THE ZECCA AND PONTE DELLA PESCHERIA (7459). Fig. 25.

Pen (Q) in black/brownish-black ink with grey wash over pencil (ruled) and pin-pointing; $6\frac{5}{16} \times 9\frac{3}{8}$ in. (160 × 238 mm.).

The building in the R. foreground, though it has only two stories instead of three, is plainly reminiscent of the Zecca. The artist may have been playing with the idea of a two-storied building to balance the Prigioni, which adjoin the Doge's Palace on the East, and have the Ponte della Paglia in a similar position to what in the drawing is doubtless intended for the Ponte della Pescheria. Further to the L. the artist anticipates the removal of the Granai (see above, p. 31) and its substitution by a terrace and garden on similar lines to those actually carried out in Napoleonic times. The embellishments of the bridge are of course purely fanciful; but behind the statue on R. the two richly decorated windows hark back to reality, the South side of the Procuratie Nuove having in fact two such windows treated in a more finished style, while the rest, hidden from view by the Granai, were left undecorated.

53. VENICE: S. MARIA DELLA SALUTE WITH THE DOGANA BEYOND (7461). Plate 22.

Pen (QM) in brown ink over pencil (freehand and ruled) and pin-pointing; $7\frac{3}{8} \times 10\frac{5}{8}$ in. (189 × 273 mm.). Some ruled ink lines occur in the foreshortened house-front on L. ; the outlines of the two domes are drawn in ink with the compasses.

Exhibited by the Magnasco Society in 1929 (No. 24). The execution is similar to that of No. 45. The drawing was doubtless made from nature (see above, p. 25), but is of a more or less standard compositional type, of which a number of versions exist as paintings. That of the former Darnley Hurcomb and Affleck Collections was in the trade about 1935, and showed, like several others of its kind, a *traghetto* in the L. foreground, the view-point being somewhat nearer to the Salute.

54. VENICE: IL REDENTORE (7483). Plate 21.

Pen (Q) in brown ink over pencil (freehand and ruled) and pin-pointing; 7⅜ × 10⅝ in. (188 × 271 mm.). There are a few ruled ink lines, and the dome of the Redentore is drawn with the compasses.

The view is drawn from near the confluence of the Canale della Giudecca and the Canale di S. Marco. The church on the extreme L. is S. Giorgio Maggiore, and that to R. of the Redentore, S. Giacomo, now demolished (see Lorenzetti, p. 723). The same view, but from a much more distant point, may be seen on the extreme L. of Plate 33. The present drawing tends to falsify the distance between S. Giorgio and the Redentore, and makes hardly any suggestion of the intervening Canale della Grazia, which separates the Giudecca from the South-Western side of the island of S. Giorgio.

55. VENICE: THE CAMPANILE DAMAGED BY LIGHTNING, 1745 (7426). Frontispiece.

Pen (Q) in brown/brownish-black ink with grey wash over pencil (chiefly ruled) and pin-pointing; 16¾ × 11½ in. (425 × 292 mm.). The ruler was used a little for drawing the pavement. In the L. upper corner is an autograph inscription (the only one of its kind) that has almost invariably been misquoted. Its true reading is *Adi 23 aprile 1745 giorno di S. Giogio Caualier/diede la saeta nel Canpanil di S. Marco.*

The day mentioned in the inscription (23 April, 1745) on which the tower was struck by lightning, and the fact that sufficient time had already elapsed since the accident for the scaffolding to be erected and the work of repair commenced, provide a useful *terminus post quem* for the date of Canaletto's departure from Venice on his first journey to England. There is no known painting that connects with the drawing; but in the British Museum is a further version of the drawing (1910.2.12.25; repr. Vasari Society, Part VIII, plate 10) that differs little in size (451 × 288 mm.), and shows only comparatively minor modifications (it has no clouds; there are workmen on the scaffold and cradle; the revolving angel at the summit of the tower faces to L., etc.). It has generally been accepted as genuine (*Burlington Magazine*, Vol. I (1903), pp. 347/8), and by Hadeln as probably so (p. 13), with emphasis, however, on its weaker execution. It has a prominent watermark of the 'Strasbourg Lily' type (W. A. Chamberlain, 400/28), which is of Dutch origin; though never met with among Canaletto's drawings made in Italy, it occurs repeatedly in those of his English period. The brown ink shows a 'run' effect, much as in Nos. 72/3, etc., which accounts for the statement that the washes are of bistre and pale indigo; there seems definitely to be a little pin-pointing. All things considered, it seems right to assume that this version, though noticeably inferior to that at Windsor (which was probably, but not certainly, drawn direct from nature), is a subsequent, but original replica, made after the artist's departure from Venice.

56. VENICE: PIAZZA S. MARCO, FACING S. GEMINIANO AND THE PROCURATIE VECCHIE (7433). Fig. 26.

Pen (QM) in brown/brownish-black ink with grey wash over pencil (freehand and ruled) and pin-pointing; 7½ × 10⅝ in. (191 × 271 mm.). The design is enclosed within a ruled ink border-line.

This drawing connects closely with one of almost exactly equal size in the Louvre (formerly in the Barnard Collection), which shows the same view towards the North-West corner of the Piazza, but extends the scene considerably on the R. side. The figures are less crowded but similar in style. Two sun-blinds project from the steeply foreshortened façade of the Procuratie Nuove on L. The quality is excellent, the technique the same. A reproduction is in *Le Dessin par les grands Maitres*, 1911, plate I/X. It is interesting to confront No. 56 with No. 6. From the latter it does not become apparent that the church of S. Geminiano did not occupy a central position in the frontage enclosing the Piazza to the West. Again, the present drawing shows the twin columns with which its façade was treated; but it suppresses the large circular window above the doorway. The rectangular structure, seen against the skyline, surmounting the roof of the building immediately to the L. of the church, was a sort of open platform in which the church bells were suspended. It is more clearly represented in Carlevarij's etching, No. 22 of his *Fabriche e Vedute*, 1703.

FIG. 26. VENICE: PIAZZA S. MARCO, FACING S. GEMINIANO (CAT. NO. 56)

57. VENICE: S. MARCO SEEN FROM THE ARCADE OF THE PROCURATIE NUOVE (7427). Plate 37.

Pen (QM) in black ink with bluish-grey wash over pencil (freehand and ruled) and much pin-pointing; 7$\frac{13}{16}$ × 11$\frac{3}{16}$ in. (193 × 284 mm.). The arches of the Basilica show a preliminary incising with the point of the dividers. The design is enclosed within a ruled ink borderline.

Exhibited by the Magnasco Society in 1929 (No. 19). Another version of this drawing was listed by Hadeln (p. 14) when in the collection of Mr. O. Gutekunst. It is now the property of Mr. Villiers David, of Friar Park, Henley. It compares favourably in quality with the Windsor version. Like a further version, formerly in the Reveley Collection (plate 19 of the Delamotte-Hardwick publication, 1858), it differs from the Windsor drawing by showing a greater expanse of the frontage of the Procuratie Vecchie, and by including one of the domes of St. Mark's and more of the upper platform of the Campanile. A distinct *pentimento* in the Windsor version shows that the tower was originally intended to stand more to the L. The brilliantly handled picture, No. 2516, of the National Gallery shows essentially the same differences as those mentioned above, but, being of an upright shape, it extends only as far as the corner of the Piazza di S. Basso on the L., and does not include the Orologio or Procuratie Vecchie. The foreground figures on R. are essentially the same, but the standing gentleman is holding a cup and saucer, a vivid touch which relates the figures with the adjacent Caffè Florian.

FIG. 27. VENICE: THE PIAZZETTA FROM THE MOLO (CAT. NO. 58)

58. VENICE: THE PIAZZETTA FROM THE MOLO (7436). Fig. 27.

Pen (QM) in black ink with bluish-grey wash over pencil (freehand and ruled) and pin-pointing; $7\frac{13}{16} \times 11\frac{1}{8}$ in. (199×282 mm.). Some ruled ink lines occur in the pavement, and a ruled border-line encloses the design.

The view may be compared with Nos. 25 and 63; the column supporting the lion of St. Mark is obviously misplaced. The treatment is dull and mechanical, and resembles No. 59, also Nos. 109 and 110.

59. VENICE: THE STEPS OF THE MOLO WITH THE PIAZZETTA BEYOND (7435). Fig. 28.

Pen (QM) in black ink with bluish-grey wash over pencil (freehand and ruled) and pin-pointing; $7\frac{15}{16} \times 11\frac{5}{16}$ in. (202×287 mm.). The design is enclosed within a ruled ink border-line.

Companion drawing to the preceding. The sizes are approximately the same, the technique identical, and the treatment similar, though a trifle less mechanical.

FIG. 28. VENICE: THE STEPS OF THE MOLO WITH THE PIAZZETTA BEYOND (CAT. NO. 59)

(60-62)

On this group, see above, p. 25. The salient feature of the drawings is their capricious distortion of spatial distances, while their architectural features are essentially accurate in rendering. The effect produced is rather like that of viewing the scenes through inverted binoculars. It remains a moot point whether they were fancifully conceived or actually seen by the artist through a combination of lenses.

60. VENICE: THE LIBRERIA AND CAMPANILE SEEN ACROSS THE PIAZZETTA (7438). Fig. 29.

(Pen QM) in black/brownish-black ink over pencil (freehand and ruled) and much pin-pointing; $9\frac{15}{16} \times 14\frac{13}{16}$ in. (227×394 mm.). A horizontal line near the R. lower corner seems to have been drawn with the ruler.

Hadeln describes the view as from a window in the Doge's Palace.

FIG. 29. VENICE: THE LIBRERIA AND CAMPANILE SEEN ACROSS THE PIAZZETTA (CAT. NO. 60)

61. VENICE: THE PROCURATIE VECCHIE SEEN ACROSS THE PIAZZA DI S. MARCO (7424). Fig. 31 (on page 42).

Pen (QM) in black/brownish-black ink over pencil (ruled) and pin-pointing; $7\frac{1}{4} \times 14\frac{7}{8}$ in. (184×378 mm.). A number of ink lines are drawn with the ruler.

There is a drawing by Bellotto at Darmstadt (Fritzsche, VZ 18; repr. Hadeln, plate 68) which is somewhat similar, and seems to have been copied from a drawing by Canaletto resembling the present one, but nevertheless distinct from it. The Basilica is included on the extreme R. and the Procuratie Vecchie are made to appear less remote. It is viewed from a point nearer to the South-Eastern corner of the Piazza.

62. VENICE: THE PIAZZETTA AND PIAZZA FROM NEAR THE TORRE DELL' OROLOGIO (7422). Fig. 30.

FIG. 30. VENICE: THE PIAZZETTA AND PIAZZA (CAT. NO. 62)

Pen (QM) in dark brown ink over pencil (freehand and ruled) and pin-pointing; $7\frac{3}{16} \times 14\frac{7}{8}$ in. (183×377 mm.).

There is a yellowish tone over the façade of S. Geminiano which looks as if the pen-work had been lightly washed over with brush and water. The ruler was used for drawing the flagstaffs and pavement lines. There is a ruled horizontal line above the top of the Campanile, drawn with pencil and marked off with pin-points.

FIG. 31. VENICE: THE PROCURATIE VECCHIE SEEN ACROSS THE PIAZZA (CAT. NO. 61)

The Darmstadt Collection contains a rather coarsely drawn outline version of this subject, by Bellotto (Fritzsche, VZ 31; repr. Hadeln, plate 69, and *Stift und Feder*, 1928, plate 87).

63. VENICE: THE CAMPANILE AND ADJACENT BUILDINGS FROM THE BACINO DI S. MARCO (7447). Fig. 32.

Pen (Q) in black/brownish-black ink over pencil (freehand and ruled) and pin-pointing; $10\frac{5}{16} \times 14\frac{9}{16}$ in. (263 × 371 mm.). The design is enclosed within a decorative border of ruled lines.

Companion drawing to No. 64; see the following note.

64. VENICE: THE PONTE DI RIALTO SEEN FROM THE EAST (7466). Fig. 33.

Pen (Q) in black/brownish-black ink over pencil (freehand and ruled) and pin-pointing; $10\frac{3}{8} \times 14\frac{7}{16}$ in. (264 × 367 mm.). The lower outline of the arch of the bridge is drawn in ink with the aid of the compasses. There is a decorative border as in the last.

Companion drawing to No. 63. The sizes correspond almost exactly, and both drawings share the unusual feature of being enclosed within a decorative border of ruled lines. In both cases this is actually part of the design, and drawn in precisely the same ink. While the technique, including the use of pencil, ruler, compasses and pin-pointing, conforms closely with the Master's usage, the execution is dull and mechanical, and it is hard to suppress some doubt whether it can really be Canaletto's. See above, p. 18. It is possible, however, that the drawings were made for the purpose of being engraved, and that this explains both their inferior quality and the presence of the unusual borders.

(65-68)

This group consists of some of the most sensitive and beautiful of Canaletto's drawings. They were certainly made as an end in themselves and from nature; no replicas, copies or related pictures are known to exist. They are here placed at the end of the Venetian series for no other reason than that they lead on from the section of Venetian views proper to that of views of the outlying islands. Entirely free of mannerisms, they must be earlier in date than their position would imply, not later, presumably, than the latter part of the 'thirties. The closest affinities that they show with other drawings are with Nos. 72, 73. It is interesting to observe that pin-pointing does not occur.

65. VENICE: VIEW IN THE SESTIERE OF DORSODURO (7486). Plate 38.

Pen (Q) in brown ink with grey wash over pencil (freehand and ruled); $6\frac{3}{16} \times 13\frac{11}{16}$ in. (156 × 348 mm.). There are a few ink lines drawn with the ruler (extreme R.).

Exhibited by the Magnasco Society in 1929 (No. 27). Opinion has differed on the locality represented. While Hadeln describes it as a view across the island of S. Elena, the sites of the Giardino Pubblico of to-day, and of S. Pietro di Castello, have also been suggested. The identification here followed is that of sig. F. Mauroner, who recognizes the churches as S. Maria Maggiore, the Chiesa dell' Angelo Raffaele, and S. Sebastiano, with the distant coastline of the Giudecca behind. He assumes the view-point to have been near the now demolished church of S. Marta.

66. VENICE: VIEW OF THE CITY FROM THE PUNTA DI S. ANTONIO (7456). Plate 39.

Pen (Q) in brown ink and grey wash, (?) over pencil traces); $6\frac{3}{16} \times 13\frac{11}{16}$ in. (156 × 346 mm.). The ruler was extensively used. There has been rather extensive 'running' of the brown ink (cp. No. 72).

Hadeln's statement that this view was drawn from the Lido is obviously incorrect. Actually it is across the Bacino from a point somewhere near the Motta di S. Antonio, that is the site of the Giardino Pubblico of to-day. Behind the rigging of the large sailing vessel S. Giorgio Maggiore is

FIG. 32. VENICE: THE CAMPANILE AND ADJACENT BUILDINGS (CAT. NO. 63)

FIG. 33. VENICE: THE PONTE DI RIALTO (CAT. NO. 64)

seen; more to the L. are the churches of the Giudecca (Le Zitelle and Il Redentore), and on the extreme L. the Euganean Hills are visible in the far distance.

67. ISOLA DI S. ELENA AND THE LAGOON (7488). Plate 40.

Pen (Q) in brown ink with grey wash over pencil (traces: freehand and ruled); $6\frac{1}{8}\times13\frac{13}{16}$ in. (155×352 mm.). There are a few ink lines drawn with the ruler.

Exhibited at Burlington House, 1930, No. 822, and reproduced by Popham, plate CCLXVII A. The view is presumably from a spot near to the Punta della Motta. The island of S. Elena has now been completely vandalized, and consists of the so-called Quartiere Vittorio Emanuele. For modern photographs, see *Italia Artistica*: *Le Isole della Laguna Veneta*, pp. 33, 34. Compare the following drawing.

68. ISOLA DI S. ELENA AND THE DISTANT COASTLINE OF THE LIDO (7487). Plate 41.

Pen (Q) in brown ink with grey and delicate pale brown washes; $6\frac{3}{16}\times13\frac{11}{16}$ in. (157×348 mm.). Near the L. lower corner is an erasure.

The prominent group of buildings in centre is certainly the same as that on the R. in No. 67, but seen from a different angle. In the distance, near the extreme R., is a small church, readily recognizable as S. Maria Elisabetta di Lido (cp. *Italia Artistica: Le Isole della Laguna Veneta*, p. 44). It stands on the water-front near the present-day landing stage of the *vaporetti.*

69. MURANO: THE CHURCH OF S. GIOVANNI BATTISTA (7458). Plate 43.

Pen (QM) in black ink over pencil (freehand and ruled) and pin-pointing; $10\frac{5}{8}\times14\frac{7}{8}$ in. (270×378 mm.).

Listed by Hadeln (p. 21) under the title '*North-West End of the Grand Canal*' (? referring to the Canal Grande of Murano). Exhibited at Burlington House in 1930 (No. 819), and reproduced by Popham, plate CCLXIV (No. 316; '*View probably taken from Murano*'). The view, in point of fact, is across the Canal Grande di Murano to the church (demolished in 1833) of S. Giovanni Battista dei Battuti (*not* S. Maria degli Angeli). A similar, somewhat smaller drawing of beautiful quality, in line and wash, passed with the Koenigs Collection to the Boymans Museum at Rotterdam (repr. *Meisterzeichnungen aus der Slg. Franz Koenigs*, Prestel XV, 1933, plate 20; and by Hadeln, plate 41). In the Windsor drawing the distant panorama of Venice with the campanile of S. Francesco della Vigna prominent on the sky-line is more spread out than in the other version. Compare the photographic panorama in *Italia Artistica: Le Isole*, facing p. 86. A drawing by Francesco Tironi in the Albertina (Stix and Fröhlich-Bume, Cat. No. 360) shows the same church. The text of Prestel XV confuses this drawing with No. 70 and the version in line and wash of the latter subject, now in the Ashmolean Museum.

70. AN ISLAND IN THE LAGOON (7491). Plate 42.

Pen (QM) in black/greyish-black ink over pencil (freehand and ruled); $7\frac{7}{16}\times10\frac{1}{2}$ in. (191×274 mm.).

The drawing in line and wash recorded by Hadeln as being in the Gutekunst Collection was presented in 1947 in memory of Mr. Otto Gutekunst to the Ashmolean Museum. It renders the house by the waterside on a slightly larger scale, but differs completely in the figures and other accessories, also in the buildings in the distance on L. A picture, formerly in the Lovelace Collection (Sotheby, 13 July, 1937, No. 129) is essentially the same as the Oxford drawing. According to Mrs. H. F. Finberg (*Burlington Magazine*, LXXII (1938), plate A, facing p. 69) there is an engraving of 1742 by Joseph Wagner of this subject (an impression is in the Correr Museum) which is accompanied by the couplet *Quanto piu bella appare/Presso alla terra il mare.* Another washed drawing of this composition has recently been in the trade; it is certainly a copy, probably English, which closely follows the Oxford drawing, but is manifestly much inferior to it in quality. The Lovelace picture was one of a set of eight, formerly at Ockham Hall, on one of which the date 1754 occurs. Hadeln describes the scene as 'at Murano', but in point of fact it may well be fanciful. On the confusion between Nos. 69 and 70 in the text of part XV of the Prestel Society, see the preceding note.

71. A CLUMP OF TREES ON AN ISLAND IN THE LAGOON (7495). Fig. 34.

Pen (M) in black ink with red chalk over pencil (traces); $7\frac{13}{16}\times10\frac{3}{16}$ in. (199×268 mm.).

As with No. 70, it is uncertain whether the view is realistic or imaginary. It is conceivable that the locality represented might be the island of Le Vignole (between S. Elena and S. Erasmo). The prominence of red chalk is an unusual feature; see above, p. 23.

FIG. 34. A CLUMP OF TREES ON AN ISLAND IN THE LAGOON (CAT. NO. 71)

(72-84)

The Paduan views, though much less numerous, are second only to the Venetian in merit and interest within the wider group of Italian topography. Unlike the Venetian, these drawings have no counterparts among Canaletto's original paintings; and even with paintings of Canaletto's school, only very few connexions are to be found. The group, on the other hand, is very closely linked with Bellotto's early series of etchings (Fritzsche VR 1-8), and the accepted date of these latter, about 1742, provides a definite terminus ante quem *which agrees well with the stylistic evidence of the drawings themselves.*

72. PADUA: THE PRATO DELLA VALLE (L. HALF) WITH S. GIUSTINA (7509). Plate 53.

Pen (QM) in brown and black inks; point of the brush in grey with grey washes over pencil (ruled) and pin-pointing; $10\frac{11}{16}\times14\frac{3}{4}$ in. (272×374 mm.). A red chalk horizon-line, drawn with the ruler, extends from margin to margin. The outline of the dome on L. seems to have been incised with the dividers. Certain passages in the foreground have somewhat the effect of a brown wash, which seems in fact to be due to an accidental running of the brown pen-work.

See the note to No. 73.

73. PADUA: THE PRATO DELLA VALLE (R. HALF) WITH THE CHURCH OF THE MISERICORDIA (7510). Plate 54.

Pen (QM) in brown and black inks; point of the brush in grey with grey wash over pencil (traces) and pin-pointing; $16\frac{3}{4} \times 14\frac{3}{4}$ in. (273 × 375 mm.). There is a red chalk horizon line as in No. 72; the same effect of brown wash, probably due to running, is noticeable. A ruled ink line occurs along the base of the arcade on the extreme R.

It is not impossible that originally Nos. 72 and 73 formed one large drawing which was cut into halves. Mr. L. Goldscheider has shown that they could be joined fairly exactly if one assumed a narrow vertical strip to have been lost in the process of bisection. In any case, of course, a continuous view was intended, though its two halves were not drawn from precisely the same spot. As in No. 89, we have here the close preparatory studies for etchings by Canaletto, viz., *S. Giustina in prà della Vale* and *Prà della Valle* (Pallucchini and Guarnati, 6 and 7; De Vesme 8 and 7). Both the etchings are somewhat larger than the corresponding drawings. Intended though they obviously were to join together, the two halves of the etched view were always distinct and separate, and there can be no question of a single plate having been cut. The view embraces what is to-day the Piazza Vittorio Emanuele, seen from the North-East. The general effect of breadth has been accentuated, and the scene is rendered as if viewed from an elevation. In No. 73 only four arches of the Collegio Universitario on the extreme R. are visible, as compared with six in the corresponding etching. In both the etchings, moreover, the scale of the buildings is slightly increased. There are minor differences among the figures. A painting in the Poldi-Pezzoli Museum, attributed to Bellotto (Fritzsche, VG 2), derives freely from the etchings and joins them into one. The handling of the drawings resembles somewhat that of Nos. 65-68.

74. PADUA: DISTANT VIEW OF S. ANTONIO FROM THE RAMPARTS (7506). Plate 48.

Pen (QM) in black/brown ink over pencil (freehand); $7\frac{7}{8} \times 11\frac{7}{16}$ in. (200 × 289 mm.). There is an autograph inscription on the reverse *Antonio Canale/Vada. . . .* This is the only drawing in the series that is fully signed (see above, p. 22).

The view resembles No. 75, but is not so extensive.

75. PADUA: DISTANT VIEW OF S. GIUSTINA AND S. ANTONIO FROM THE RAMPARTS (7505). Plate 49.

Pen (QM) in black/brown ink over pencil (freehand and ruled) and pin-pointing; $10\frac{11}{16} \times 14\frac{7}{8}$ in. (272 × 378 mm.).

A copy in outline by Bellotto is at Darmstadt (repr. Hadeln, plate 70; Fritzsche, VZ 54). The view is drawn from the West and shows (from L. to R.) S. Giustina, Porta Ponte Corvo, S. Antonio (in centre), S. Daniele, Torre Ezzelino, S. Francesco (far R.) and the Palazzo della Ragione (extreme R.). For a more detailed view of S. Francesco, see No. 80. This last, as well as No. 75, should be confronted with a drawing (No. 3) forming part of a series of 18 small and very summary sketches in the Viggiano Collection at Venice. In the lower part of this appear S. Francesco and the Salone; near the L. upper corner is the Porta Ponte Corvo, inscribed *Coruo,* after which is an abbreviated inscription which may be interpreted as *questa misura a destra sino Sa. Giustina,* a dotted line indicating the appropriate distance from the extremity of the church.

76. PADUA: S. GIUSTINA FROM THE RAMPARTS (7499). Plate 55.

Pen (QM) in black/greyish-black ink over pencil (freehand and ruled); $7\frac{7}{16} \times 10\frac{11}{16}$ in. (189 × 272 mm.). A ruled horizon-line is drawn with pencil from margin to margin.

An outline drawing in the British Museum (1910.2.12.26) corresponds in all details; it is accepted as genuine by Hadeln, but, though its quality is not bad, it fails to convince, and is more probably by Bellotto. A drawing by Bellotto at Darmstadt (Hadeln, plate 67; Fritzsche VZ 49) shows a closely dependent composition; it served as a preliminary study for Bellotto's etching, Fritzsche VR 2. Two figures, however, are added near the L. extremity of the foreground on R.; there is a horseman in centre, and a large tree on R. To L. of the Porta Ponte Corvo, moreover, a church, somewhat resembling the Santo, has been added, and a small building with a gabled roof abuts upon the gatehouse, as in No. 79. The etching reverses the drawing, with the result that the church resembling the Santo comes to stand in approximately its right position in relation to S. Giustina. But as a whole, of course, the scene is capriciously transposed.

FIG. 35. PADUA: S. GIUSTINA FROM THE RAMPARTS (CAT. NO. 77)

77. PADUA: S. GIUSTINA FROM THE RAMPARTS (7500). Fig. 35.

Pen (QM); in black/greyish-black ink over pencil (freehand and ruled); $7\frac{3}{8} \times 10\frac{3}{4}$ in. (188 × 272 mm.).

The view should be compared with No. 76. Bellotto's etching, Fritzsche VR 4, is essentially the same, but in reverse. A drawing by Bellotto at Darmstadt (Fritzsche, VZ 51) is a preparatory study for the etching, but in the same direction; it is a reduced and reversed copy of our Windsor drawing, No. 77.

78. PADUA: OUTSKIRTS OF THE CITY (7542). Plate 51.

Pen (QM) in black/greyish-black ink over pencil (freehand and ruled) and pin-pointing; $10\frac{5}{8} \times 14\frac{7}{8}$ in. (270 × 378 mm.).

Although Hadeln describes this subject as a 'Village church . . . on the Terra Ferma', the view is obviously of Padua, and to all appearance a *veduta esatta.* The tower resembles that of S. Giustina; the gate-house of the Porta Ponte Corvo is unmistakable. Bellotto's etching, Fritzsche VR 6, reverses the principal features of the drawing, and adds a prominent tower to the building on the extreme L., interposing the arches of a loggia between the foreground and more distant view. This latter feature is borrowed from Canaletto's etching, Pallucchini-Guarnati No. 11.

FIG. 36. PADUA: OUTSKIRTS OF THE CITY (CAT. NO. 79)

79. PADUA: OUTSKIRTS OF THE CITY (7501). Fig. 36.

Pen (QM) in black ink over pencil (freehand and ruled) and pin-pointing; $7\frac{7}{16} \times 16\frac{11}{16}$ in. (189×271 mm.). There is a touch of red chalk to indicate the level of the window in the gate-house on R.

There are two outline copies by Bellotto at Darmstadt (Fritzsche, VZ 48 and 45). The latter is the more carefully executed. The former served the artist as a working design for his etching, Fritzsche VR 5, which reverses the scene and introduces certain minor modifications: it omits the tree near the extreme R. of the drawing, and substitutes a crenellated tower for the belfry in the centre distance.

80. PADUA: S. FRANCESCO WITH DISTANT VIEW OF THE SALONE (7502). Fig. 37.

FIG. 37. PADUA: S. FRANCESCO WITH DISTANT VIEW OF THE SALONE (CAT. NO. 80)

Pen (QM) in black/greyish-black ink over pencil (freehand and ruled); $7\frac{3}{8} \times 10\frac{11}{16}$ in. (187×272 mm.). There is a ruled horizon line drawn with pencil from margin to margin.

An outline copy, apparently by Bellotto, said to be from the Darmstadt collection, was in Fischer's Sale at Lucerne, 2 June, 1945, lot 10 (plate 2 of catalogue). The church is identical with the one appearing at some distance to the R. of the Santo in No. 75 (Plate 49) and inscribed *Uicino il Sa°* in the lower portion of the sketch in the Viggiano Collection, mentioned in the note to No. 75. As pointed out by Fritzsche (*Graphische Künste, Mittlg.*, 1930, p. 51), our drawing, No. 80, seems to have been freely used by Canaletto himself for the unique etching at Windsor (Pallucchini-Guarnati, No. 30), in which the church is rendered in reverse against a mountainous background, and with a fanciful foreground which includes the motive of a statue on a rectangular pedestal.

81. PADUA: VIEW OF THE OUTSKIRTS WITH THE TORRE DI EZZELINO AND S. ANTONIO (7507). Plate 47.

Pen (QM) in black/grey ink over pencil (freehand and ruled) and a little pin-pointing; $10\frac{11}{16} \times 14\frac{7}{8}$ in. (272×377 mm.).

The crenellated tower is clearly the same as in Nos. 74/5, Bellotto's etching, Fritzsche VR 5, and elsewhere. Though it does not correspond in every detail, it clearly resembles the Ezzelino tower as rendered before its demolition, in certain drawings of the early XIX century, repr. *Italia Artistica: Padua*, 1912, p. 49.

82. PADUA: THE PORTELLO AND BRENTA CANAL (7504). Plate 56.

Pen (QM) in black/brown ink over pencil (freehand and ruled); $10\frac{5}{8} \times 14\frac{3}{4}$ in. (270×375 mm.). There is a long diagonal line drawn with the pen and ruler on L.

The view is roughly to the North-West, the Porta Portello (now Porta Venezia) being on the Eastern periphery of the city. The distant church, a little to R. of centre, is S. Maria del Carmine. Fritzsche lists a copy by Bellotto at Darmstadt (VZ 55). A washed drawing, recently in the trade, is manifestly a copy, perhaps English. There is another drawing in line and wash in the Albertina (Catalogue Stix-Bume, 1926, No. 358), certainly by Canaletto himself; this, however, is viewed not from directly above the canal, but from a point more to the L. A similar item was in the Elton Sale (Sotheby, 13 November, 1924, lot 98). A picture of this same type, of fine quality, and doubtless an early work of Bellotto, is in the collection of Mr. F. F. Madan.

83. PADUA: PALAZZO DELLA RAGIONE (7503). Plate 52.

Pen (QM) in black ink over pencil (freehand and ruled) and pin-pointing; $7\frac{1}{2} \times 10\frac{11}{16}$ in. (199×271 mm.). The chevron signature occurs near the extreme L., below the obelisk surmounting the angle of a palace.

The view is across the Piazza delle Erbe with the Municipio on the R. The scene is freely rendered and by no means topographically reliable.

84. PADUA: A VILLA ON THE OUTSKIRTS OF THE CITY (7514). Plate 50.

Pen (QM) in black/brown ink with grey wash over pencil (freehand and ruled) and pin-pointing; $12\frac{3}{8} \times 15\frac{11}{16}$ in. (314×399 mm.). The five arches of the loggia on L. are incised with the point of the dividers. The design is enclosed within a ruled ink border-line.

The drawing is particularly sensitive and masterly in execution. It shows no direct relation to any other recorded *veduta*, whether drawing or picture or etching. It might very well be from nature. Though hard to locate at all closely, it has every appearance of being topographically exact. The roof of the Salone appears on R.

85. PADUA: (?) THE RIVIERA DI S. BENEDETTO (7511). Plate 57.

Pen (M) in black/greyish-black ink over pencil (freehand); $5\frac{2}{3} \times 7\frac{2}{3}$ in. (138 × 186 mm.). There is a curious pencil scribble across the sky. On the reverse is a very slight pencil sketch showing an urn on a tall pedestal L., and a tomb or tabernacle on R.

The tentative identification of the scene was suggested by sig. F. Mauroner. In the distance one sees what is apparently the Torre di Ezzelino and the tower of the Carmini. Hadeln professes to see unusual features in the technique, but in fact it does not seem to deviate at all strikingly from what is normal. The reverse sketch, apparently for a *capriccio*, is unimportant in itself, but is interesting as showing a preliminary lay-out which the artist evidently discarded and left unfinished.

86. PADUAN CAPRICCIO: (?) THE RIVIERA DI S. BENEDETTO IN FANCIFUL SETTING (7513). Plate 58.

Pen (M) in brown ink with grey wash over pencil (freehand and ruled) and pin-pointing; $8\frac{1}{2} \times 14\frac{13}{16}$ in. (215 × 377 mm.). The outlines of the three arches are incised with the point of the dividers. There is a fingerprint at the lower margin about 4 in. from the L. corner.

The L. half of the composition corresponds closely with No. 85. The R. half has every appearance of being a fanciful extension. An outline copy by Bellotto (Fritzsche VZ 123, plate 15) is in the Boymans Museum. It was formerly in the Darmstadt, Goldschmidt and Koenigs Collections.

87. BRIDGE OVER A RIVER (THE BRENTA OR BACCHIGLIONE?) (7498). Plate 59.

Pen (QR) in grey/brownish/grey-black ink over pencil (freehand and ruled) and pin-pointing; $8\frac{3}{4} \times 12\frac{13}{16}$ in. (223 × 325 mm.).

See the note on the following drawing.

88. BRIDGE OVER A RIVER (THE BRENTA OR BACCHIGLIONE?) (7497). Plate 60.

Pen (MQ) in grey/brownish/black ink over pencil (freehand and ruled), red chalk (foreground and column) and pin-pointing; $7\frac{3}{8} \times 10\frac{3}{4}$ in. (187 × 273 mm.).

The two drawings, Nos. 87 and 88, are essentially alike, but the latter is a little more finished, and has the feature, no doubt fanciful, of a column surmounted by the lion of St. Mark in the L. foreground. They are connected, more or less closely, with certain other works by Canaletto in various media, which are listed below:

(A) Two panoramic sketches, originally joined, in pen and red chalk, one of which is in the Fogg Art Museum, and the other in the Morgan Library. See *Old Master Drawings*, Vol. XIII (1938), p. 34. It should be noted that the whereabouts of these two drawings have been confused, i.e., that the drawing stated by A. Mongan, Pallucchini-Guarnati, and others, to be in Boston, is really in New York, and *vice versa*. The reproduction, moreover, given by Pallucchini-Guarnati (p. 23), shows the two halves wrongly joined together, and should be transposed in order to show the correct positions of the two halves.

(B) The etching listed by De Vesme, Fritzsche, and Pallucchini-Guarnati as No. 9.

(C) The painting, formerly in the collection of Sir John Foley Grey, now the property of Mr. Mark Oliver.

The Fogg Museum drawing is signed and dated 1742 on the reverse; apart from this, however, it is of no direct interest to us in connexion with the Windsor drawings, Nos. 87 and 88, since it does not cover the same sector of the view. The Morgan Library portion, on the other hand, shows the same bridge and water-wheels, and a similar grouping of houses, but *not* the distant campanile. While the Fogg Museum and Morgan Library panorama is evidently an accurate rendering from nature, the Windsor drawings have apparently omitted certain superfluous details in the interests of pictorial clarity. The campanile appearing in the two latter is presumably a fanciful addition, transferred from the extreme L. of the Fogg Museum drawing, i.e., from roughly the middle of the panorama when the two halves are correctly joined. The etching gives an accurate, but reversed rendering of the whole scene (that is with the campanile near the centre, not immediately above the head of the bridge as at Windsor, nor on the extreme L. as in the wrongly joined reproduction given by Pallucchini-Guarnati). The foreground of the etching resembles Windsor 87/88 in the motive of the tree cutting across the line of lower buildings; but in the former it is larger and more in the manner of Ricci. Mr. Oliver's picture, so far as the buildings are concerned, corresponds exactly with the etching, but in reverse. It differs in the figures, omits various accessory details, but shows the planked bridge at the side. It is reproduced in the Sachs-Mongan Catalogue of the Fogg drawings, p. 155. Another painting, at Parma (Congregazione di S. Filippo Neri) is simply a copy of the etching (repr. *Inventario . . . Prov. di Parma*, 1934, p. 134). The exact site of the view cannot be established with accuracy, but is probably (as assumed by Pallucchini-Guarnati) at Padua, *not* at Dolo or elsewhere on the Brenta.

(89-101)

The drawings here grouped together show no consistent affinity to one another in style or execution, but all are evidently scenes on the Brenta, and they thus constitute a geographical unit covering the Venetian terraferma from the seaboard to Padua.

89. MESTRE: THE EXTREMITY OF THE CANALE DELLE BARCHE (7490). Plate 61.

Pen (Q) in greyish ink over pencil (freehand and ruled) and pin-pointing; 10 × 16 in. (255 × 407 mm.). A ruled horizon-line drawn with red chalk extends from margin to margin, and on it are markings at intervals of equal distance.

This is a study for Canaletto's (somewhat larger) etching inscribed *Mestre* (De Vesme 3; Pallucchini-Guarnati 5). It corresponds fairly closely; apart from the omission of the flying birds and a few minor changes among the figures, the etching differs essentially from the drawing at only one point, namely the house on the extreme L. (thought by De Vesme to be a Customs office, but an inn according to Pallucchini-Guarnati). Here, instead of only three arches, the etching shows the wider frontage of five. Whereas Hadeln (p.23) accounts for this difference by assuming that the drawing has been cut, Pallucchini-Guarnati are of a different opinion, and consider it possible that the artist extended the etching in order to increase the expanse of white of the façade of the building. In point of fact, it is practically certain that the drawing has not been mutilated. It is out of the question that a cut was made on the R. side, corresponding with that suspected on the L.; but it will be seen on close inspection that one of the markings on the horizon-line coincides exactly with the centre of the page. There is, moreover, a vertical crease which also runs through the centre, as if a folded page, like that of a drawing book, had been used. Furthermore, the top of the coach is, in the drawing, on precisely the same level in relation to the third arch (from R.) as it is to the fifth in the etching. It is safe, then, to assert that the assumption of Hadeln and Fritzsche is incorrect. A painting of this subject is in the collection of the late Sir George Leon, Bracknell, Berks. It has the greater breadth of the etching, but considerably less sky, and shows notable differences in the figures.

90. A COUNTRY HOUSE ON THE VENETIAN TERRAFERMA (7549). Plate 62.

Pen (QM) in black/grey ink over pencil (freehand and ruled) and a little pin-pointing; $9\frac{15}{16} \times 16$ in. (253×406 mm.). The steeply receding lines near the L. lower corner seem to have been drawn with the aid of the ruler.

The subject does not occur again in any other medium. The execution is similar to that of No. 89.

91. (?) DOLO: A SLUICE-GATE ON THE CANAL (7496). Fig. 38.

Pen (QR) in black/greyish-black ink over pencil (freehand and ruled); $8\frac{3}{4} \times 12\frac{7}{8}$ in. (234×327 mm.).

Though accepted by Hadeln (p. 24 and plate 33) as the work of Canaletto, the drawing was said by Fritzsche

FIG. 38. (?) DOLO: A SLUICE-GATE ON THE CANAL (CAT. NO. 91)

(*Graphische Künste, Mittlg.*, 1930, p. 19) to be more in the manner of Bellotto. This is by no means convincing; in fact, it accords well in style with Nos. 89 and 90. The view is probably at Dolo, and Pallucchini-Guarnati support this contention on the evidence of Canaletto's etching (No. 3) and another (II/XI) of the series *Delle Delicie del Fiume Brenta*, 1756, by G. F. Costa. The assumption is very plausible, but it must be admitted that there is no close correspondence, and that if the place is really the same, the *darsena* is represented from a different viewpoint.

92. PALAZZO TRON AT DOLO (7551). Plate 63.

Pen (QR) in black/light brownish ink over pencil (freehand and ruled); $8\frac{13}{16} \times 12\frac{7}{8}$ in. (224×328 mm.).

Though generally thought to represent the Villa Pisani at Strà, this drawing, and Nos. 93 and 94, are certainly of the Palazzo Tron, as is proved by the exact correspondence of all architectural features, including the octagonal pavilion, with plate 64 of G. F. Costa's *Delle Delicie del Fiume Brenta*, 1756. The general design of No. 92 is more or less the same as that of No. 93; it has analogous figures in the foreground, while, unlike in No. 94, the barge is in both cases close to the remoter bank. It is interesting to observe that there are ruled pencil lines, one of which is vertical, just to L. of the barge, the other, horizontal, roughly at shoulder-level of the foreground figures. These lines seem to anticipate the more compactly enclosed design of No. 94.

FIG. 39. PALAZZO TRON AT DOLO (CAT. NO. 93)

93. PALAZZO TRON AT DOLO (7553). Fig. 39.

Pen (Q) in black/grey ink over pencil (freehand and ruled) and pin-pointing; $6\frac{15}{16} \times 10\frac{3}{16}$ in. (176×257 mm.).

See the note on the preceding drawing. This is the smallest and sketchiest of the three versions of the scene, and resembles more nearly No. 92.

94. PALAZZO TRON AT DOLO (7552). Fig. 40.

Pen (QR) in black/brownish-black/grey ink over pencil (freehand and ruled); $7\frac{5}{16} \times 10\frac{1}{2}$ in. (186×267 mm.). The roof of the octagonal pavilion shows scratching on R.

A copy, somewhat larger, by Bellotto is listed by Fritzsche as being at Darmstadt (VZ16). For general remarks, see the note on No. 92. Although Hadeln asserts that the view-point is different, it is in fact to all intents and purposes the same, though the foreground in the L. half of the design is made to appear closer to the opposite bank. The view is more restricted at the L. margin, whereby the palace is given a central position. The barge bulks larger; the carriage is replaced by a waggon drawn by oxen.

FIG. 40. PALAZZO TRON AT DOLO (CAT. NO. 94)

FIG. 41. A VILLA ON THE BRENTA (CAT. NO. 95)

95. A VILLA ON THE BRENTA (7550). Fig. 41.

Pen (QR) in black/greyish-brown ink over pencil (freehand and ruled) and a little pin-pointing. A ruled horizon-line is visible on L. It is possible that the ruler was used in conjunction with the pen to draw the horizontal below the roof of the distant house on the extreme R.

The villa could not be identified, but was evidently, like Nos. 92-94, one of the patrician summer residences on the Brenta.

96. A CHURCH, PRESUMABLY ON THE VENETIAN TERRAFERMA (7512). Fig. 42.

Pen (MQ) in black/greyish-black ink over pencil (freehand and ruled) $7\frac{7}{16}\times10\frac{11}{16}$ in. (189×272 mm.).

A copy in outline, no doubt by Bellotto, said to come from the Darmstadt Collection, has recently been in the trade.

97. THE PAVILION OF A VILLA ON THE VENETIAN TERRAFERMA (7515). Plate 44.

Pen (M) in black ink; $6\frac{9}{16}\times9\frac{1}{2}$ in. (176×243 mm.).

Exhibited by the Magnasco Society, 1929, No. 26. Whether the drawing is a *veduta esatta* is less certain than with the others of this group. The building has been variously described as a villa and church, but actually it seems to be a *casino* within the encircling walls of the grounds of a larger country residence. See the note on No. 98. On the reverse is an unimportant sketch (pen over pencil) of sailing vessels at their moorings, which may or may not be the work of Canaletto.

FIG. 42. A CHURCH ON THE VENETIAN TERRAFERMA (CAT. NO. 96)

98. THE PAVILION OF A VILLA ON THE VENETIAN TERRAFERMA (7543). Plate 45.

Pen (QM) in black/brownish black ink with bluish-grey wash over pencil (freehand and ruled) and a little pin-pointing; $8\times11\frac{1}{2}$ in. (205×292 mm.). The design is enclosed within a ruled ink border-line.

This is a somewhat larger version of No. 97 in a more elaborate technique and more mannered style. The connexion was overlooked by Hadeln. There are various minor differences: the flying birds are omitted, and the wide projecting balcony or terrace adjoining the pavilion in No. 97 is replaced by a low roof with chimneys.

99. A VILLA WITH A GARDEN STATUE IN THE FOREGROUND (7554). Fig. 43.

Pen (QM) in black/grey ink over pencil (freehand and ruled); $5\frac{7}{16}\times7\frac{3}{4}$ in. (136×198 mm.).

FIG 43. A VILLA WITH A GARDEN STATUE IN THE FOREGROUND (CAT. NO. 99)

The drawing is closely related to Nos. 100 and 101; all are, no doubt, 'exact' and from nature. The villa, which could not be identified, was almost certainly on or near the Brenta. It shows no resemblance to that at Mogliano belonging to Consul Smith, as represented in drawings by Antonio Visentini at Windsor. The motive of the statue on a tall rectangular pedestal is similar to that in the unique etching by Canaletto at Windsor, Pallucchini-Guarnati, No. 30.

100. GARDEN STATUES IN THE GROUNDS OF A VILLA (7556). Fig. 44.

Pen (QM) in black/greyish-black ink over pencil (traces); $5\frac{3}{8}\times7\frac{13}{16}$ in. (137×197 mm.).

The place is evidently the same as in No. 99, and the statue on R., which seems to be a Hercules resting his club across his shoulder, might be identical with the last.

101. GARDEN STATUES IN THE GROUNDS OF A VILLA (7555). Fig. 45.

Pen (QM) in black ink over pencil (freehand); $5\frac{3}{8}\times7\frac{3}{4}$ in. (136×197 mm.). On R. a leaning tree, sketched in pencil,

FIG. 44. GARDEN STATUES IN THE GROUNDS OF A VILLA (CAT. NO. 100)

has been omitted from the drawing as carried out with the pen.

Probably the same place as represented in Nos. 99 and 100. There is a similar statue of Hercules in centre.

(102-113)

This group is covered by an important article by T. Ashby and W. G. Constable in Burlington Magazine, *XLVI (1925, pp. 207-214, 288-299), and comprises the Roman views, whether topographically exact or partly fanciful. It does not include, however, purely imaginary compositions of a more or less Roman appearance. As already stated (p.25), even the faithful delineations show no signs of being actually drawn from nature. In two cases it has been shown that Canaletto copied Étienne Du Pérac (T. Ashby,* Topographical Study in Rome in 1581, *Roxburghe Club, 1916). It is probable that the artist visited Rome on two occasions: first in or about 1719 (for which there is the evidence of Zannetti:* ciò fu circa l'anno 1719 . . . passò giovinetto a Roma, e tutto si diede a dipingere vedute dal naturale); *the second time in or about 1742 (a conjecture made plausible by H. Voss,* Repertorium f. Kw. *XLVII (1926), p. 21, and confirmed on other evidence by Pallucchini-Guarnati, pp. 27, 28). A series of 22 small drawings in the British Museum (1858.6.26.221-242), to which belongs a further page separated from the rest at Darmstadt, show manifold connexions with the Windsor Roman views. They all have marginal 'signatures' of Canaletto, and their authenticity was accepted by Ashby and Constable* (Burl. Mag., *XLVI (1925), p. 294), but rejected by Hadeln (p. 1, note 1). There is can be no serious doubt that the latter's verdict was correct. In spite of their outward resemblances to drawings listed below, their execution is feeble, and shows none of the characteristics either of Canaletto's early style, such as we know it, or of his maturity.*

FIG. 45. GARDEN STATUES IN THE GROUNDS OF A VILLA (CAT. NO. 101)

102. ROME: DISTANT VIEW OF S. MARIA IN COSMEDIN AND PONTE ROTTO (7516). Plate 64.

Pen (QM) in black ink over pencil (freehand and ruled) and pin-pointing; $10\frac{5}{8} \times 14\frac{7}{8}$ in. (270×376 mm.).

See Ashby and Constable, p. 293. The bridge in the foreground is the Ponte dei Quattro Capi. There are three drawings in the British Museum of this view, but with slightly differing accessories. It occurs with only very minor differences as No. 240 of the series of small drawings, referred to above, which, though accepted by Ashby and Constable, are rejected by Hadeln. This, it would appear, was either copied from the Windsor drawing or its immediate prototype. Then there is a fine and certainly original version in line and wash, somewhat larger (more especially in its height measurement) than the Windsor drawing, in which, however, the coach is moving in the opposite direction, that is from L. to R. (repr. *Burl. Mag.* XLVI, p. 292, plate B). Another drawing in line and wash (1878.12.28.2) was considered to be probably original by Ashby and Constable, but rejected by Hadeln. In the writer's opinion it is a manifestly English copy of the early XIX century, closely following 1910.2.12.23.

103. ROME: THE ARCH OF SEPTIMIUS SEVERUS WITH S. ADRIANO (7538). Plate 65.

Pen (QM) in black ink over pencil (freehand and ruled) and pin-pointing; $9\frac{11}{16} \times 14\frac{13}{16}$ in. (238×376 mm.). A ruled horizon-line is drawn with pencil from margin to margin.

The drawing is based on, but not exactly copied from, an engraving (No. 3) in Étienne Du Pérac's *Vestigi delle Antichita di Roma*, 1575; see T. Ashby in the *Roxburghe Club Publication* of 1916, p. 22, where the engraving and drawing are reproduced as plates 3 (Fig. 4) and 4 respectively. Ashby here confuses Windsor 7538 with 7496; this same drawing (No. 103) is again wrongly numbered (but as 7527) in *Burlington Magazine*, XLVI (1925), p. 294. Hadeln repeats the latter error. There is a version in outline at Munich (repr. *Handz. alter Meister*, plate LXXVIII, Hadeln, plate 40), which is almost certainly by Bellotto, though accepted as genuine by Hadeln. Ashby and Constable admit its weakness and cast doubt on its authenticity.

104. ROME: THE TEMPLE OF ANTONINUS AND FAUSTINA (7522). Plate 66.

Pen (QM) in black/brownish black ink over pencil (freehand and ruled) and pin-pointing; $9\frac{3}{8} \times 14\frac{13}{16}$ in. (238×376 mm.).

Like the preceding drawing, this is based on, but not exactly copied from, an engraving (No. 4) in Étienne Du Pérac's *Vestigi delle Antichità di Roma*, 1575; see *Roxburghe Club Publication*, 1916, p. 22, plates 3 (Fig. 5) and 5. (The Windsor drawings 7522 and 7485 are there confused.) Apart from differences of perspective, etc., Du Pérac's view of the East side of the Forum extends further to the R., and includes the whole façade of SS. Cosma e Damiano of which the drawing shows little more than the tower.

105. ROME: THE FORUM WITH THE BASILICA OF CONSTANTINE AND S. FRANCESCA ROMANA (7525). Fig. 46.

Pen (QM) in black ink over pencil (freehand and ruled) and pin-pointing; $10\frac{11}{16} \times 14\frac{7}{8}$ in. (271 × 378 mm.).

The same view, but in upright format, is represented in a picture of fine quality, certainly by Canaletto himself, in the Collection of the late Sir George Leon (from the Trotter Collection). The figures differ, but there is some correspondence of accessories. A picture by Bellotto in the Borghese Gallery (*Burl. Mag.*, XLVI (1925), p. 213, plate 212 G; Fritzsche VG 6) is, like the drawing, oblong, but resembles the Leon picture in the squatter proportions of the tower, which is somewhat fancifully rendered in the drawing. There is an etching of the Borghese picture by Brustolon. The view also occurs in the series of small drawings in the British Museum (1858.6.26.226).

106. ROMAN CAPRICCIO: THE TEMPLE OF SATURN IN FANCIFUL SETTING (7520). Plate 68.

Pen (QM) in black/dark brown ink over pencil (freehand and ruled) and pin-pointing; $10\frac{5}{8} \times 14\frac{13}{16}$ in. (270 × 376 mm.).

FIG. 46. ROME: THE BASILICA OF CONSTANTINE AND S. FRANCESCA ROMANA (CAT. NO. 105)

Ashby and Constable (*Burl. Mag.*, XLVI (1925), p. 294) describe the Roman elements of the drawing as 'quite fancifully composed.' The temple resembles (in reverse) that on the R. of Bellotto's etching, Fritzsche VR 7 (repr. pl. facing p. 40, in upper centre), but neither the architectural details nor perspective are identical. It seems, nevertheless, that Bellotto used both the present drawing and No. 125 for the print in question. A picture, called Bellotto, in the Museo Civico at Asolo (Venice Exhib., 1946, *Capolavori dei Musei Veneti*, No. 306) shows the temple in a different and even more capricious setting.

107. ROMAN CAPRICCIO: THE TEMPLE OF VESPASIAN IN FANCIFUL SETTING (7521). Plate 67.

Pen (QM) in black/dark brown ink over pencil (freehand and ruled) and pin-pointing; $10\frac{3}{8} \times 14\frac{3}{4}$ in. (265 × 375 mm.). The ruler was used in conjunction with the pen to draw the lance of the seated man in the R. lower corner, and that of the man nearby, entering the gateway of the church.

Ashby and Constable (*Burl. Mag.*, XLVI (1925), p. 294) describe the background as 'entirely fanciful.'

FIG. 47. ROME: THE TEMPLE OF VENUS AND ROME WITH S. FRANCESCA ROMANA (CAT. NO. 108)

108. ROME: THE TEMPLE OF VENUS AND ROME WITH S. FRANCESCA ROMANA (7524). Fig. 47.

Pen (M) in black/greyish-black ink; $7\frac{7}{16} \times 16\frac{5}{8}$ in. (189 × 271 mm.). The ruler was used in conjunction with the pen for drawing the tower of S. Francesca. The chevron signature occurs in centre, above the arch of the temple.

One of the series of small drawings in the British Museum (1858.6.26.237) shows the same subject, but with variations in the background, and the arch of Titus less prominent in the L. distance. See Ashby and Constable, *Burl. Mag.*, XLVI (1925), p. 294.

109. ROME: PIAZZA DI S. GIOVANNI IN LATERANO (7517). Fig. 48.

Pen (QM) in black/greyish-black ink with pale grey wash over pencil (chiefly ruled) and pin-pointing; $7\frac{13}{16} \times 11\frac{3}{16}$ in. (200 × 285 mm.). The design is enclosed within a ruled ink border-line.

This drawing and No. 110 are companions, and correspond closely to one another, and to Nos. 58 and 59, in size, style and technique. The same view, from the distant aqueduct of Nero on L. to the Obelisk and Lateran Palace, occurs in the series of small drawings in the British Museum (1858.6.26.241). One of the pictures of the Lovelace series, sold at Sotheby's, 13 July, 1937 (No. 128), is again the same view, but extends further to R. and includes the Lateran

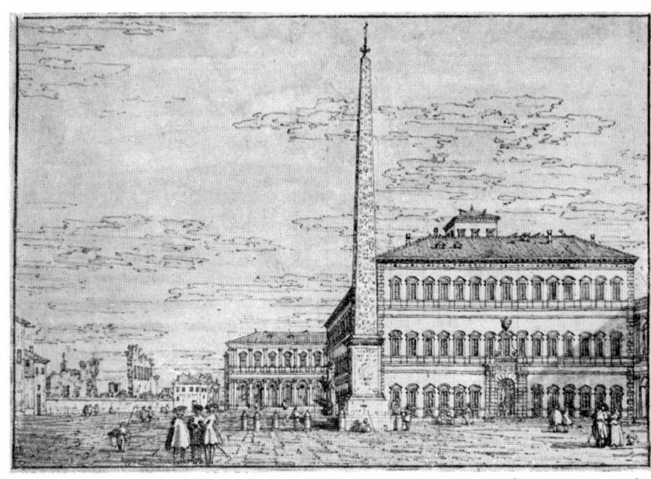

FIG. 48. ROME: PIAZZA DI S. GIOVANNI IN LATERANO (CAT. NO. 109)

Church. In spite of various minor modifications, it shows the triangle of shadow across the R. lower corner of the palace.

FIG. 49. ROME: SS. DOMENICO E SISTO (CAT. NO. 110)

110. ROME: SS. DOMENICO E SISTO (7518). Fig. 49.

Pen (QM) in black ink with grey wash over pencil (freehand and ruled) and much pin-pointing; $7\frac{7}{8} \times 11\frac{1}{8}$ in. (200 × 283 mm.). The design is enclosed within a ruled ink border-line.

Companion to No. 109. It resembles No. 234 of the series of small drawings in the British Museum (1858.6.26). The dome of St. Peter's on the extreme L. is obviously capricious, both as regards its position and architectural detail.

111. ROME: (?) THE CALDARIUM OF THE BATHS OF CARACALLA (7531). Fig. 50.

Pen (QM) in black ink over pencil (freehand and ruled) and pin-pointing; $7\frac{1}{2} \times 11\frac{1}{16}$ in. (191 × 281 mm.). The design is enclosed within a ruled ink border-line.

This item is wrongly listed by Hadeln (also by Ashby and Constable) as 7532. The drawing corresponds with No. 232 of the series of small Roman subjects in the British Museum (1858.6.26; repr. *Burl. Mag.*, XLVI (1925), plate 295E), which is inscribed *Caldario Terme Antoniane.* The identification is somewhat questionable, but the building seems not to be fanciful.

FIG. 50. ROME: (?) THE CALDARIUM OF THE BATHS OF CARACALLA (CAT. NO. 111)

112. ROMAN CAPRICCIO: THE ARCO DEI PANTANI IN FANCIFUL SETTING (7519). Fig. 51.

Pen (Q) in black/brownish-black ink with grey wash over pencil (freehand and ruled) and pin-pointing; $7\frac{5}{8} \times 10\frac{13}{16}$ in. (194 × 274 mm.). The outline of the arch below on R. is incised with the point of the dividers. The subject is enclosed within a ruled ink border-line.

An aquatint by F. C. Lewis appeared as plate LXVI of J. Chamberlaine's *Original Designs of the most celebrated Masters . . . in His Majesty's Collection*, 1812. This was listed under Bellotto by R. Weigel, *Die Werke der Maler in ihren Handzeichnungen*, 1865, p. 69, No. 772. In addition to the arch, the temple of Mars Ultor, which appears behind it, is in the main topographically correct, but the vaulting in the foreground and arch on R. are fanciful, while the campanile of S. Basilio, the forum of Augustus and the Torre del Grillo have been capriciously omitted. A more accurate rendering is No. 242 of the series of small drawings in the British Museum (1858.6.26) which is reproduced *Burl. Mag.*, XLVI (1925), plate 292D.

113. ROMAN CAPRICCIO: THE ARCH OF TITUS IN FANCIFUL SETTING (7523). Plate 83.

FIG. 51: ROMAN CAPRICCIO: THE ARCO DEI PANTANI (CAT. NO. 112)

Pen (QM) in black/brown ink with grey wash over pencil (freehand and ruled) and pin-pointing; $7\frac{11}{16} \times 10\frac{13}{16}$ in. (195 × 274 mm.). The design is enclosed within a ruled ink border-line.

Ashby and Constable (*Burl. Mag.* XLVI, p. 294) describe the *background* as fanciful, but clearly the foreground and building adjacent to the arch are equally so. They mention (*ibidem*, p. 208) a picture, formerly at Bath House (a photograph in the B.M.), which they believe to have derived from the present drawing. It shows, in point of fact, only a very remote resemblance, and there is certainly no direct connexion. See below, No. 133.

(114-119)

Canaletto's English period is at present the best documented of his career, mainly as the result of the researches of Mrs. H. F. Finberg, published by the Walpole Society (Vol. IX (1920/21), pp. 22-76). A terminus post quem *for his departure from Venice is provided by the drawing No. 55 of the present series, which proves that for some time after the 23 April, 1745, he was still in his native city. According to Vertue (Finberg, p. 27) he arrived in London at the 'latter end of May,' 1746, but in 1750/51 (p. 35) 'made a tour of his own country . . . for some affairs there in 8 months going and comeing.' His final return to Venice from London was, according to Pietro Gradenigo, on 28 July, 1753, but, in the light of other evidence, in 1755. The six views of London, all of which, except one, show Old Westminster Bridge and architectural features more or less accurately dateable, are not, however, among the drawings that are convincingly from nature. See above, p. 25. It follows that the dates assignable to them are only approximate, and that it may well be that they were actually of later execution than would, on the face of it, appear.*

114. LONDON: VIEW OF THE CITY FROM THE TERRACE OF SOMERSET HOUSE (7560). Plate 69.

Pen (Q) in black/greyish-black ink with grey wash over pencil (freehand and ruled) and much pin-pointing; $7\frac{7}{8}\times 19\frac{1}{16}$ in. (200×485 mm.). The arches of the landing-stage are incised with the point of the dividers. The design is enclosed within a ruled ink border-line.

Exhibited at the Burlington Fine Arts Club, 1919, No. 5. Listed by H. F. Finberg, *Walpole Society*, IX, p. 64. Companion drawing to No. 115. The view shows the spires of the City churches with St. Paul's on the L. and Old London Bridge in the far distance, on R. There is a painting by Canaletto at Windsor (Collins Baker, p. 47, plate 13; Burlington House Exhib., 1946/47, No. 475) which shows essentially the same view, but as if from a somewhat greater elevation. It has more sky and foreground, and, though analogous, differs considerably in the figures and shipping. It may well have been executed in 1750/51, while the artist was in Venice. Another picture, no longer traceable, originally in the collection of Thomas West, was engraved by E. Rooker and published in 1750 and 1751. The assumption that these paintings were actually based on the present drawing is almost certainly incorrect, and shows a misconception of the purpose of carefully finished drawings of the type in question. A considerably larger drawing in line and wash (237×711), which shows closer correspondence with the Windsor drawing than does the picture at Windsor, was in the Fauchier Magnan Sale (Sotheby, 4 Dec., 1935, lot 3) and now belongs to Count Anton Seilern. It is certainly preferable to the other in the quality of its execution.

115. LONDON: VIEW OF WESTMINSTER FROM THE TERRACE OF SOMERSET HOUSE (7559). Plate 71.

Pen (Q) in black/greyish-black ink with grey wash over pencil (freehand and ruled) and much pin-pointing; $8\frac{13}{16}\times 19\frac{1}{8}$ in. (223×486 mm.). The design is enclosed within a ruled ink border-line.

Exhibited at the Burlington Fine Arts Club, 1919, No. 7. Listed by H. F. Finberg, *Walpole Society*, IX, pp. 73-74. The view shows Westminster Bridge, completely finished, in the centre distance; more to the R. are St. John's Church, the House of Commons and the Abbey, and near the extreme R. the Banqueting House in Whitehall and the tower of the Waterworks. As in the case of No. 114, there is a similar picture at Windsor (Collins Baker, p. 48, plate 14; Burlington House Exhib., 1946/47, No. 438); but it is viewed from a higher point and renders the parapet of the terrace in the R. foreground in steeper perspective. The figures are different, but there are analogies in the shipping. Another version, now lost, was formerly the property of Thomas West; it was engraved by J. S. Muller and published in 1751. A considerably smaller picture than that at Windsor, and more nearly related than it to the drawing, belongs to the Duke of Hamilton.

116. LONDON: WESTMINSTER BRIDGE WITH DISTANT VIEW OF LAMBETH PALACE (7558). Plate 73.

Pen (Q) in black/greyish-black ink with grey wash over pencil (ruled) and much pin-pointing; 9×19 in. (227×484 mm.). The outline of each of the arches of the bridge was incised with the point of the dividers. A *pentimento* is visible at the centre arch, where there is an incised segment a little to the R. of that drawn over with the pen. Another incised segment of the same radius occurs above the centre arch at the level of the horizon. The design is enclosed within a ruled ink border-line.

Exhibited at the Burlington Fine Arts Club, 1919, No. 4. Listed by H. F. Finberg, *Walpole Society*, IX, p. 71. The drawing is there dated *about* 1747 on the evidence that the bridge still lacks some of the turrets surmounting the piers of the arches. The view is rendered as from a considerable elevation above the water on the Surrey side. St. John's, the House of Commons, Westminster Hall, the Abbey and St. Margaret's appear to R. of the Archbishop's Palace, seen in the far distance, centre. The British Museum has a larger drawing (1868.3.28.305; repr. Finberg, pl. XVI) from the same view-point, but showing the bridge in a finished state and with different shipping. A picture belonging to the Duke of Buccleuch (Finberg, pl. XV) is from above mid-stream; all the piers of the bridge are completed. It was engraved by Remigius Parr and published in 1747. Another picture, in the possession of Mr. Thomas Bodkin, was exhibited at the Burlington Fine Arts Club, 1936/37, No. 108, and reproduced in colour in the *Studio* of June, 1924 (Vol. 87, plate facing p. 303). Here the view-point is exactly as in the Windsor drawing, but the bridge is completed and has all its turrets. The shipping differs.

117. LONDON: WESTMINSTER BRIDGE WITH A PROCESSION OF CIVIC BARGES (7557). Plate 75.

Pen (Q) in black/greyish-black ink with grey wash over pencil (freehand and ruled) and pin-pointing; $10\frac{13}{16}\times 19\frac{1}{8}$ in. (274×486 mm.). The design is enclosed within a ruled ink border-line.

Exhibited at the Burlington Fine Arts Club, 1919, No. 8. Listed by H. F. Finberg (*Walpole Society*, IX, pp. 71, 72), who dates the drawing *about* 1747. As in No. 116, some of the turrets surmounting the piers of the arches are unfinished. The view is from the Surrey bank. The procession of barges is, according to Mrs. Finberg, the state progress to Westminster of the Lord Mayor, on 29 October. A similar, but larger drawing of the finished bridge is in the British Museum (1857.5.20.61).

118. LONDON: WESTMINSTER BRIDGE UNDER CONSTRUCTION (7562). Plate 76.

Pen (Q) in black/greyish-black ink with grey wash over pencil (traces) and much pin-pointing; $11\frac{9}{16}\times 19\frac{1}{16}$ in. (293×484). The outline of the largest arch was perhaps incised with the point of the dividers. The subject is enclosed within a ruled ink border-line.

Exhibited at the Burlington Fine Arts Club, 1919, No. 12, and by the Magnasco Society, 1929, No. 29. Listed by H. F. Finberg, *Walpole Society*, IX, p. 73. The view is from the Westminster side of the river, and shows the rebuilding of the fifth pier and the fourth and fifth arches after a subsidence in 1747 (shortly before the bridge was due to be opened) of the original construction, commenced in 1738/39. The purely topographical evidence points, therefore, to a date somewhere about 1749/50.

119. LONDON: ST. PAUL'S SEEN THROUGH AN ARCH OF WESTMINSTER BRIDGE (7561). Plate 77.

Pen (Q) black/brownish-grey ink and grey wash over pencil (traces) and much pin-pointing; $11\frac{3}{8}\times19\frac{1}{16}$ in. (298×484 mm.). The design is enclosed within a ruled ink border-line.

Exhibited at the Burlington Fine Arts Club, 1919, No. 10, and by the Magnasco Society, 1929, No. 28. Listed by H. F. Finberg, *Walpole Society, IX*, p. 71 (plate XIIa). A replica, certainly by Canaletto himself, was published by W. G. Constable in *Old Master Drawings*, Vol. IV (1929), p. 5, plate 11; it figured as lot 48 of the Henry Oppenheimer Sale, Sotheby, 16 July, 1936. It is a trifle larger in scale and more oblong in format, but differs only very slightly in details. The view extends from the wooden tower of the Waterworks on L. to St. Paul's on R., with the spires of St. Mary-le-Strand and St. Clement Dane's prominent against the sky-line. A picture belonging to the Duke of Northumberland (repr. Finberg, pl. XIIb) shows practically the same panorama, but through an arch which is still supported by its wooden understructure. This picture is dated by Finberg at 1747, in which year an engraving of it by Remigius Parr was published. According to Charles Labelye's *Description of Westminster Bridge*, 1751, the last arch was keyed in July, 1746, and this earlier year would therefore seem the more probable, that is on evidence purely topographical. For the Windsor and Oppenheimer drawings it provides merely a *terminus post quem*. Constable inclines to the belief that the Windsor version is the earlier of the two, since 'in his later English drawings Canaletto tends to use line more freely than wash.' This contention, however, is somewhat debatable.

(120-140)

Here are grouped together the purely fanciful views, or vedute ideate, *as opposed on the one hand to views that are topographically more or less accurate, and on the other to those showing some degree of realism, albeit capriciously distorted. See above, p. 25. In some few cases (Nos. 121, 122) the distinction from 'capricci' is a narrow and perhaps arbitrary one. The majority show the mannered style associated with the artist's maturity and later period.*

120. VEDUTA IDEATA WITH REMINISCENCES OF CHIOGGIA (7540). Plate 46.

Pen (Q) in brown ink with grey wash over pencil (freehand and ruled) and (?) pin-pointing; $9\frac{7}{8}\times14\frac{5}{16}$ in. (251×379 mm.). The arches of the bridge are incised with the point of the dividers. In the L. half of the composition the ink seems to have run.

Exhibited at Burlington House, 1930, No. 821, and reproduced by Popham, plate CCLXVI. The view is certainly not realistic: the belief that the ancient bridge of Brondolo at Chioggia is represented, cannot be upheld. The towers in the distance, however, are not unlike those of S. Andrea and the Duomo, and it is possible that the artist was visualizing an imaginary junction between Chioggia Maggiore and Chioggia Minore.

121. VEDUTA IDEATA WITH REMINISCENCES OF MURANO (7492). Fig. 52.

Pen (QM) in black ink over pencil (freehand and ruled) and a little pin-pointing; $7\frac{1}{2}\times10\frac{11}{16}$ in. (190×272 mm.). The flagstaff is drawn with the aid of the ruler.

FIG. 52. VEDUTA IDEATA WITH REMINISCENCES OF MURANO (CAT. NO. 121)

Hadeln describes this and the following drawing as views of S. Donato at Murano. There are certainly resemblances (cp. *Italia Artistica: le Isole della Laguna Veneta*, 1925, pp. 103, 104); but none of the topographical details are sufficiently close to warrant a classification among the *vedute esatte*.

122. VEDUTA IDEATA WITH REMINISCENCES OF MURANO (7493) Fig. 53.

Pen (QM) in black/greyish-black ink with bluish-grey wash over pencil (freehand and ruled) and a little pin-pointing; $7\frac{7}{8}\times11$ in. (198×281 mm.). The cord of the flagstaff is drawn with the aid of the ruler, and the design is enclosed within a ruled ink border-line.

The composition is similar to the preceding, but is drawn in the more elaborate technique of line and wash.

123. VEDUTA IDEATA WITH REMINISCENCES OF PADUA (7508). Plate 87.

Pen (QM) in black/brown ink with brown wash and heightening in body-colour over pencil (freehand and ruled) and pin-pointing; $10\frac{11}{16}\times15$ in. (271×381 mm.). There are a few ink lines drawn with the aid of the ruler. The flat arch on R. is incised with the point of the dividers.

The drawing is somewhat anomalous in style and handling, but its authenticity remains nevertheless unassailable. Though Hadeln (p. 6) refers only to a single drawing, at

FIG. 53. VEDUTA IDEATA WITH REMINISCENCES OF MURANO (CAT. NO. 122)

Berlin, as being heightened in body-colour, this feature is not by any means unique, and appears in all the drawings of the Mocenigo Series of 1763, which are in the British Museum, the Rosebery and ex-Oppenheimer Collections. One of a set of four painted *vedute ideate* in the Parma Gallery, attributed to Bellotto (repr. G. Delogù, *Pittori minori del Settecento*, 1930, pl. 91) is similar to the drawing in general design. A statue of Neptune replaces the urn on R., and a tall house the church to L. of the arch. The figures (by Zuccarelli) are entirely different. The Paduan reminiscences in the drawing are restricted to the campanile and crenellated tower (this latter resembling the Torre di Ezzelino). At the stage of the preliminary pencil sketch the tower on R. and adjoining fortification wall were carried to a considerably greater height.

124. VEDUTA IDEATA WITH REMINISCENCES OF PADUA AND VICENZA (7541). Plate 79.

Pen (QM) in black/brownish and grey-black ink with bluish-grey wash over pencil (freehand and ruled) and much pin-pointing; $7\frac{3}{4} \times 11\frac{1}{8}$ in. (198 × 283 mm.). There is a ruled horizon-line drawn with pencil from margin to margin. The arch of the bridge is incised with the point of the dividers. The design is enclosed within a ruled ink border-line.

FIG. 54. VEDUTA IDEATA IN THE ROMAN STYLE (CAT. NO. 125)

A close but slightly enlarged copy in outline by Bellotto is in the Berlin Print Room (Fritzsche, VZ 66; repr. Hadeln, plate 65). The view, though essentially fanciful, seems to include definite reminiscences of the Torre di Ezzelino and Palladian buildings.

125. VEDUTA IDEATA IN THE ROMAN STYLE (7532). Fig. 54.

Pen (QM) in black/brownish/grey ink with pale bluish-grey wash over pencil (freehand and ruled) and pin-pointing; $7\frac{13}{16} \times 11\frac{1}{16}$ in. (199 × 280 mm.). The design is enclosed within a ruled ink border-line.

This is wrongly listed by Hadeln as No. 7533. The view is classified as fantastic by Ashby and Constable (*Burl. Mag.* XLVI, p. 294). Fritzsche (p. 142) points out that both this drawing and No. 106 were used by Bellotto for his etching, VR7, where the motive of the ruined dome occurs, somewhat modified and in reverse, on L. There is a pen drawing at Darmstadt in reverse to the etching (repr. *Stift und Feder*, 1928 (63).

FIG. 55. VEDUTA IDEATA IN THE ROMAN STYLE (CAT. NO. 126)

126. VEDUTA IDEATA IN THE ROMAN STYLE (7536). Fig. 55.

Pen (QM) in black ink over pencil (traces); $7\frac{7}{16} \times 10\frac{3}{4}$ in. (188 × 272 mm.). Fig. 56.

This is wrongly listed by Ashby-Constable and Hadeln as No. 7537. The view seems to be purely imaginary.

127. VEDUTA IDEATA IN THE ROMAN STYLE (7535). Fig. 56.

Pen (QM) in black/dark brown ink over pencil (traces); $7\frac{1}{2} \times 10\frac{3}{4}$ in. (190 × 273 mm.). A ruled horizon-line is drawn in pencil from margin to margin.

This is wrongly listed by Hadeln as No. 7536. Ashby and Constable (*Burl. Mag.* XLVI, p. 294) pronounce the view to be purely imaginary. The composition recurs in No. 128.

128. VEDUTA IDEATA IN THE ROMAN STYLE (7529). Fig. 57.

Pen (Q) in black/grey ink with grey wash over pencil (freehand and ruled) and much pin-pointing; $7\frac{11}{16} \times 10\frac{3}{4}$ in. (195 × 273 mm.). The arches were incised with the point of the dividers. The design is enclosed within a ruled ink border-line.

This is wrongly listed by Hadeln as No. 7530. The composition is essentially the same as No. 127.

FIG. 56. VEDUTA IDEATA IN THE ROMAN STYLE (CAT. NO. 127)

FIG. 57. VEDUTA IDEATA IN THE ROMAN STYLE (CAT. NO. 128)

129. VEDUTA IDEATA IN THE (?) ROMAN STYLE (7527). Fig. 58.

Pen (QM) in black/brownish-black ink over pencil (traces); $7\frac{7}{16} \times 10\frac{11}{16}$ in. (189×272 mm.).

This is wrongly listed by Hadeln as No. 7528. It is not referred to by Ashby and Constable, and it may be doubted whether the ruin was intended by the artist to be Roman. The drawing listed both by Ashby-Constable and Hadeln as 7527 is in fact 7538 (i.e., No. 103 of the present catalogue).

130. VEDUTA IDEATA: A FOUNTAIN ON THE SHORES OF A LAGOON (7537). Plate 80.

Pen (QM) in black ink over pencil (traces); $7\frac{7}{16} \times 10\frac{3}{4}$ in. (190×274 mm.). The chevron signature occurs on the pedestal of the fountain.

This is wrongly listed by Hadeln as No. 7538. The composition is no doubt purely imaginary; it approximates somewhat to a *capriccio* in the sense of Guardi. See above, p. 25. This is one of the drawings, like Nos. 1-4, etc., which show a yellowish stain over the centre of the page, while the pasted edges are not discoloured. See p. 18, note 25.

131. VEDUTA IDEATA: A MEDIEVAL TOMB AMID CLASSICAL RUINS (7526). Plate 81.

Pen (QM) in black/brown ink over pencil (freehand and ruled); $7\frac{7}{16} \times 10\frac{3}{4}$ in. (199×272 mm.). The chevron signature occurs on the arch above the tomb.

FIG. 58. VEDUTA IDEATA IN THE (?) ROMAN STYLE (CAT. NO. 129)

The building in the L. middle distance is clearly reminiscent of the Colosseum. The composition, with its incongruous juxtaposition of buildings of unrelated styles, is somewhat in the nature of a *capriccio*.

132. VEDUTA IDEATA: RUINS ON A SHORE WITH MOUNTAINOUS COASTLINE (7534). Plate 78.

Pen (QM) in black ink with bluish-grey wash over pencil (freehand and ruled) and pin-pointing; $8 \times 11\frac{5}{16}$ in. (203×287 mm.). The design is enclosed within a ruled ink border-line.

This is wrongly listed by Hadeln as No. 7535. An aquatint by G. Hawkins appeared as plate LVIII of J. Chamberlaine's *Original Designs of the most celebrated Masters . . . in His Majesty's Collection*, 1812. It was listed under Bellotto by R. Weigel, *Die Werke der Maler in ihren Handzeichnungen*, 1865, No. 771.

133. VEDUTA IDEATA: A CLASSICAL ARCHWAY ON THE SHORES OF A LAGOON (7533). Plate 82.

Pen (QRM) in black/greyish-black ink with bluish-grey wash over pencil (freehand and ruled) and much pin-pointing; $7\frac{3}{4} \times 10\frac{15}{16}$ in. (198×278 mm.). The outlines of the arch and of the circular medallion are incised with the point of the dividers. Another incised segment, overlapping the

FIG. 59. VEDUTA IDEATA IN THE RUSTIC STYLE (CAT. NO. 135)

obelisk, is visible on the extreme L. The design is enclosed within a ruled ink border-line.

This is wrongly listed by Hadeln as No. 7534. Unlike No. 113, to which it bears a general resemblance, the architectural motives are purely fanciful. A somewhat similar arch occurs in a picture, formerly at Bath House, which is the companion to that referred to in connexion with No. 113. A picture, called Bellotto, almost identical in composition with the drawing, was lent by the Museo Civico of Asolo to the 1946 Venice Exhibition (*Capolavori dei Musei Veneti*, No. 307; repr. *Cat.*, p. 189).

134. VEDUTA IDEATA: RUINS OF A CHURCH ON THE SHORES OF A LAGOON (7528). Plate 86.

Pen (QM) in black/brown ink with grey wash over pencil (freehand and ruled) and a little pin-pointing; $7\frac{13}{16} \times 11\frac{5}{16}$ in. (198×287 mm.). Above the recumbent effigy are traces of pencil-work which are possibly a *pentimento*, but might also be unconnected with the actual design. On the reverse is a very slight and unimportant sketch of architecture, drawn with pencil and ruler.

This is wrongly listed by Hadeln as No. 7529. An aquatint by G. Hawkins appeared as plate LXIV of J. Chamberlaine's *Original Designs of the most celebrated masters . . . in His Majesty's Collection*, 1812. It was listed under Bellotto by R. Weigel, *Die Werke der Maler in ihren Handzeichnungen*, 1865, No. 773. A slightly reduced copy, probably English of the early XIX century, was formerly in the Albert Meyer Collection, Paris (repr. as plate 16 of Seymour de Ricci's *Dessins du XVIII siècle, Collection A.M.*, 1935). It is now in America.

135. VEDUTA IDEATA IN THE RUSTIC STYLE (7548). Fig. 59.

Pen (QM) in black ink over pencil (traces); $7\frac{7}{16} \times 10\frac{5}{8}$ in. (189×269 mm.).

The house with a walled garden and a fountain at its rear resembles, but not in all particulars, the motive of the L. half of No. 136.

136. VEDUTA IDEATA: A HOUSE AND FOUNTAIN ADJOINING A RUINED ARCH (7530). Plate 85.

Pen (QM) in black ink with bluish-grey wash over pencil (freehand and ruled) and a little pin-pointing; $7\frac{5}{8} \times 11\frac{3}{16}$ in. (195×283 mm.). The design is enclosed within a ruled ink border-line.

FIG. 60. VEDUTA IDEATA IN THE RUSTIC STYLE (CAT. NO. 137)

This is wrongly described by Hadeln as No. 7531. It is interesting that, over the spout of the fountain, an arch, similar to that in No. 135, is drawn with pencil. This shows that, in spite of variations, No. 136 was in fact based on the preceding drawing. In this connexion, cp. Nos. 46 and 47. A further *pentimento* occurs on R., where the small gabled structure on top of the arch is carried to a greater height in the pencil sketch. The statue on the column is reminiscent of the revolving angel which surmounts the campanile of St. Mark.

137. VEDUTA IDEATA IN THE RUSTIC STYLE (7547). Fig. 60.

Pen (QM) in black/brownish-black ink over pencil (traces); $7\frac{3}{8} \times 10\frac{11}{16}$ in. (188×271 mm.). There is a ruled ink horizon line in the L. half of the composition.

This is the prototype of No. 138, which shows only slight variations.

138. VEDUTA IDEATA IN THE RUSTIC STYLE (7546). Fig. 61.

Pen (QM) in greyish-black/grey ink with bluish-grey wash over pencil (freehand and ruled) and a little pin-pointing;

FIG. 61. VEDUTA IDEATA IN THE RUSTIC STYLE (CAT. NO. 138)

$7\frac{1}{2} \times 10\frac{15}{16}$ in. (191×273 mm.). The design is enclosed within a ruled ink border-line.

This is a fairly close rendering, but in a more elaborate technique and mannered style, of No. 137. It differs essentially only in the omission of the tall tree on L., and the inclusion of a further chimney at the end of the house.

139. VEDUTA IDEATA IN THE RUSTIC STYLE (7545). Fig. 62.

Pen (QM) in black/brownish-black ink over pencil (traces); $7\frac{7}{16} \times 10$ in. (189×272 mm.). There is a ruled horizon-line drawn with pencil.

The drawing is akin to the four preceding.

140. VEDUTA IDEATA: THE PAVILION AND COURTYARD OF A VILLA (7544). Plate 84.

Pen (QM) in black/brown ink with pale grey wash over pencil (freehand and ruled) and much pin-pointing: $8\frac{1}{2} \times 13\frac{5}{16}$ in. (215×338 mm.). The outline of the arch of the pavilion is incised with the point of the dividers. The chevron signature occurs in the tympanum above the keystone of the arch. The design is enclosed within a ruled ink border-line.

A late work, rather mannered and artificial, but of fine quality.

141. ARCHITECTURAL FANTASY: A FLIGHT OF STEPS LEADING TO THE LOGGIA OF A PALACE (7564). Plate 88.

FIG. 62. VEDUTA IDEATA IN THE RUSTIC STYLE (CAT. NO. 139)

Pen (QM) in black/dark brown ink with grey wash over pencil (freehand and ruled) and pin-pointing; $14\frac{1}{4} \times 20\frac{7}{8}$ in. (363 × 531 mm.). The outline of the arch, incised with the point of the dividers, was originally intended to be at a higher level, and was indicated by a further incised semicircle. A little to L. of the large stone vase in the R. foreground another *pentimento* is visible: originally a statue (indicated in pencil) was intended to surmount the pedestal. The chevron signature occurs at the angle of the loggia. The lance held by the man at the foot of the steps is drawn with the aid of the ruler. The design is enclosed within a ruled ink border-line.

The drawing was not recorded by Hadeln; see above, p. 18. It is in the nature of a perspective *tour de force*, like Canaletto's diploma picture of 1765, a drawing in the Albertina (Cat. Stix-Bume, No. 360), and other similar works.

142. ARCHITECTURAL FANTASY: A CLASSICAL GATEWAY IN A GARDEN (7563). Plate 89.

Pen (M) in brownish/dark brown ink; point of the brush in dark grey water-colour with grey wash over pencil (freehand and ruled) and much pin-pointing; $13\frac{7}{16} \times 13\frac{3}{4}$ in. (341 × 350 mm.). The outlines of the arch and of the two circular medallions are incised with the point of the dividers. The design is enclosed on three sides by a ruled ink border-line, but not along the R. edge.

The drawing was not recorded by Hadeln. It is of the *prospettiva* class, like No. 141. The use of the point of the brush is unusual, but also occurs in Nos. 73 and 143.

143. THE PORTICO OF A VILLA WITH A STATUE OF HERCULES (7539). Fig. 63.

Pen (QM) in black/brownish-black ink; point of the brush in dark grey with grey wash over pencil (freehand and ruled) and pin-pointing; $13\frac{3}{8} \times 7\frac{11}{16}$ in. (340 × 196 mm.). The design is enclosed on three sides by a ruled ink border-line, but not along the L. edge.

It seems probable that this is but a fragment of a considerably larger composition. The subject, as it stands, appears very unusual, but the execution is unmistakably Canaletto's, in spite of the uncommon use of the point of the brush, for which, however, see Nos. 73 and 142.

FIG. 63. THE PORTICO OF A VILLA WITH A STATUE OF HERCULES (CAT. NO. 143)

DOCUMENTS

(A) THE WILL OF JOSEPH SMITH

The original is in the Archivio di Stato, Venice.
It is reprinted here from the text of Horatio F. Brown
in "Notes and Queries" 10th Series, Vol. 4 (1905),
pp. 282-284; 383-384.
Only the portions printed in larger type
have direct reference to the Collections.
See above, p. 11.

I Joseph Smith late Consul of his Britannic Majesty to the most Serene Republic of Venice, humbly acknowledging the many and great mercys that God of his infinite goodness hath been pleased to bestow on me, Do make and ordain this my last Will and Testament all written with my own hand and with a reserve to myself of a Power to make therein such alterations and additions as I shall hereafter think fitt, which I will be deem'd of the same validity and force as if [they] were inserted in the Body of the writing.

First I give to my Nephew Samuel Bagwell the sum of one thousand Pounds sterling, and to his sisters, my Nieces, that is to such of them as at the time of my Decease shall not have been married, to each of them Two hundred Pounds sterling: these summs to be paid to them or to their Lawful Assigns, within the space of twelve months after my decease, and if any of them, Brother or Sisters, shall dye within the time of the said Twelve months, before these Legacys become payable Then my will is that the portion of the deceased shall be divided among the survivors according to the proportion of their respective Legacys.

Second I give and forgive to my nieces Catherine Goodenough and Esther Henley and to each of them, all and every summ and summs of money it may appear they be owing to me as heirs to my late Brother John Smith, upon Mortgage, Bond, Note or otherwise with all interests due thereon.

Thirdly I give three months wages to such of my domestic servants at Venice as shall have liv'd with me for the space of one year and likewise I give to my two Boatmen Thirty currant ducats each provided that they also shall have one year in my service, and upon the same conditions I give to my servants at Moggiano to wit Coachman, Postillion, Antonio Pasqualati and Santo, Helper in the Garden, to each of these four three months salary and to Paulo Campelli Head Servant at Moggiano I give two hundred ducats curr. All these legacys to be paid to them within a month after my decease.

Fourthly And my will is that five hundred currant ducats be given to the Pievano of the Parish of the SS. Apostoli, where I have always dwelt from my first coming to Venice, to be by him distributed to such as shall appear to him to be fit objects of Charity, particularly recommending to his prudence to have in view and to prefer such Poor as may be infirm, of either sex not under fifty years of age of which charity so distributed he is to produce proof of its being comply'd with, and this summ of five hundred ducats to be paid within two months of my decease.

Fifthly In regard that through some error, neglect or mismanagement voluntary or otherwise, during my apprenticeship with the late Mr. Thomas Williams any loss may have happened to his Estate which because of the misfortunes which afterwards oppressed him, and his Death, cannot be made good as ought and as I desired, for satisfaction of my Conscience in this Point I will that the summ of one hundred pounds sterling be apply'd to such Pious Use or Uses as my Executrix shall think fitt and within such time as may be convenient for her to do it.

Sixthly To John Yersin, to whom I have been a sincere well wisher, for which his letters, which will be found among my papers, are a sufficient Testimony, I give and forgive what he may appear from my Books in his own handwriting, to be owing to me.

Seventhly Whereas I have a debt to Mr. Santino Cambiaso, circulating by Exchange on Amsterdam, of Sixteen Thousand Bank ducats for security whereof I have deposited in his hands Effects in Jewels, Gold coins, cameos and Intaglios, which by my books appear to have been purchased (and without vanity I may say with good skill) as occasions have presented in a course of many years, and though bought with advantage, cost a much greater summ, and particularly the antient Imperial medals, the quadruple of what is assigned as their value in the note delivered to the said Cambiaso; in which among other things the Cammeos and intaglios are esteemed at D. 7000 curr^{t}, which on account of the singular excellency of many of them, and others very estimable for their fine workmanship, so that on the whole I compute this collection to be really worth double the sum expressed in the Note formed at the time this deposit was made and the delivery of the Effects to the said Cambiaso by the hands of Sig. Giovanni Antonio Albinoni according to his declaration signed and sealed, which will be found among my papers, to be confronted at the restitution of these Effects, as Sig. Cambiaso refus'd to give himself any writing or receipt when they were delivered to him by the above said Albinoni. Now my intention always was and still is, that this debt be discharged by part of the Money that will be produced from the Sale of the Books assign'd to and received by me for Capital and Profit arising from the Buisness of Bookseller and Printer carry'd on for my account by Giambattista Pasquali for the space of 24 years, amounting to the real cost nigh D. 140000 currt. according to the distinct Catalogues and Inventorys in my possession and existing in three warehouses, to wit in the warehouses at S. Gio. Crisostomo di Ca' Ruzzini in Calle della Testa and alli Mendicanti all conformably to the Lists and Accounts deliver'd in by the said Pasquali, Director of the said Buisness, and the final settlement made with him and the passing of reciprocal discharges for balance whereof he remains Dr to me the Sum of D 10,000 currt. to be paid in proportionate summs in the space of six years.

Eighthly I give to the Lady Bridget Wentworth one hundred Guineas which I desire she would accept to be employed in the purchase of a Ring and wear as a Testimony of my respect and Esteem and grateful sense of the Friendship she has honoured me with.

9thly To John Murray Esqre His Majestie's Resident at Venice I leave my gold repeating watch, made by Graham, valuable being made by that excellent artist and may be considered the more so as it was the last he made!

Xthly To the Reverend Mr. Thomas Murray I give one hundred Pounds sterling as a mark of my esteem for a very worthy man and if he consents his daughter shall live with her Aunt Elizabeth she I know will very gladly receive her and employ every propper and affectionate regard in her Education, than whom I know none more capable, in every respect, both by precept and example.

XIthly To Mr. John Udny, British Consul, I give the two Portraits and their frames, one representing the last Doge Cornaro, painted by Pietro Uberti, the other my Predecessor, Mr. Thomas Williams, painted by the celebrated Dahl, not impropper ornaments (as I hope hee'l judge) for a Place in the House he inhabits, formerly possessed by the said Mr. Williams and afterwards by myself till my removal to the house I built contiguous to it.

XIIthly Any and every just debt that may appear I may be owing I desire be discharg'd, which without my recommending to my Widow I am certain shee'l take care to do, some there may be that I dont recollect.

XIIIthly I bequeath to Mrs. Eliza Agoin of Dublin, my lesser Yellow Diamond Ring as to a person I very much esteem for her own great merit and a most intimate, loving and beloved Friend of my Wife, and provided their respective conveniencys will permit it, as I am fully persuaded would correspond to their mutual desire, I recommend to them to live together, in such place as they shall both determine.

XIVthly After the payment of my Lawful Debts and the several Legacys herein mentioned I give and bequeath all the Residue of my real and Personal Estate wherever situated and in whatever manner compos'd and of whatever kind it may be, unto my dear *wife* Mrs. Elizabeth Smith whom I wish long to survive me in the enjoyment of every solid Felicity, which while I liv'd my only aim and desire was to procure to her, and I constitute and appoint my said dear wife Elizabeth Smith sole Executrix of this my last Will and Testament, and in regard of the trouble it must entail I desire my friends Mr. John Udny, Brittish Consul, and Mr. Conraed Martens, Consul of Denmark, to be assisting to her herein, with their friendly advice and aid in order to realize such Part of my effects as she shall judge propper to form a settlement for her in such place the most to her comfort and satisfaction where [she] shall chose to reside; this Trouble I desire they would moderate and each of them to accept of one hundred ounces of silver wrought Plate and understand it to be a Testimony of Esteem and Friendship of their departed Friend.

XVthly There being prepar'd and preparing for the Press, and with a design to be made Publick, three sundry works, towards which I have already made a considerable expense, viz.,

1. 'Museum Smithianum', or be it 'Dactyliotheca Smithiana', being my collection of Gemms illustrated by the late learned Anton Francesco Gori of Florence, to which is prefixed 'Historia Glyptographica', by the same Author, of which work 500 copies in Folio are already printed.
2. 'L'architettura di Andrea Palladio,' folio, copy'd exactly from the Author's own Edition, printed at Venice in the year 1570, with no other but the ammended difference that instead of the original Plates which are engrav'd on wood in this Edition they are on copper traced with the most scrupulous precision from Palladio's original, and that to this new Edition will be prefix'd the Author's Life (now ready for the Press) wrote by Tomaso Temanza, most capable of such a work, which with great dilligence he hath been several years collecting materials for compiling, and moreover this edition will be enriched with the Portrait of Palladio engraven from an original Painting (and the only one extant in his younger years) done by Pordenone; of which work the said Portrait and the Plates (except four or five as the Engraver of them Pietro Monaco assures me) are all finished.
3. 'Gli Errori degli Architetti' by Galliccini with the additions and observations by Antonio Visentini of which work (impatiently expected by the true lovers of sound Architecture) the greatest part of the Copper Plates are finished and the rest are in hand.

Now my will is that respectively as these three works shall be published a copy of each be given to Sir James Gray Bar, His Majesties Envoy Extraordinary and Plenipotentiary at Naples, to Thomas Hollis Esq. of Bedford Row, London, and to the Abbot Dr. Facciolati, Professor in the University of Padoua, of which I desire their acceptance as a testimonial of my Esteem and respect and of my grateful sense of the friendship that for so many years they have honoured me with. These books, bound in red Marocco leather gilt and with my coat of arms impressed on their covers, be transmitted to them free of all charge, and one more copy of each in like manner I desire may be favoured with a place in the Library of John Murray Esq. the King's Resident at Venice.

I dye in perfect charity with every one and with an humble Hope to find mercy with Almighty God for my sins only by and through the Merits and Satisfaction of my Redeemer Jesus Christ.

If I dye at Venice or in the State of Venice my desire is to be bury'd at the usual Place on the Island of Lido assigned for the interment of Protestants in such decent and frugal manner as my Widow shall think fit, and the same to be observed should I happen to dye in any other country, in which case my Widow is to direct where I shall be buryed, but in whatever Place I shall happen to dye, my will and desire is not to be buryed till on the fourth day after to all appearance I shall have resigned my spirit to my Creator.

As the Principal Part of my Estate consists of the considerable collections I have made in forty years and better and allow'd by all who have examined them, to be all, in their different kinds, well chosen, and whereas my Relict will very probably be minded to realize by selling all or great part thereof, to establish thereby a decent and comfortable settlement for the remainder of her life, I think it not improper to say something upon this head by way of information and advice in such case, and so to cooperate even after I shall be no more, to her future happiness.

I was always desirous that some entire classes of my collection might remain united, such as my Library, Drawings, Gemms or Pictures, and with this view a treaty was commenced on the Part of a Royal Purchaser for my Library, according to the printed Catalogue, made public, in which that collection is brought down to the year 1752, and for which the said Treaty was upon the foot of Twenty Thousand Sequins, but by reason of the present war breaking out about that time nothing was concluded.

The Drawings consist of numbers of Original Pieces by the greatest masters, particularly are among them the three large Volumes, formerly collected in the time of the Caracci, by the family of Bonfiglioli of Bologna, and upon the Death of Sigr. Bartolomeo, were purchased by the Noble Venetian Zaccaria Sagredo, and cost 3,000 sequins, as appears by a Letter printed about that time wrote by Anton Maria Zanetti of Venice to his Friend the Cavalier Gaburri of Florence. In this collection also are four Volumes containing original drawings by Gio. Benedetto [*sic*] Castiglione great part whereof are the most capital of his Performance, these likewise belong'd to the said Nobleman Sagredo, purchased by him at twice, and it was then said cost him 1,500 sequins. Of the rest I need say nothing, but to the volumes themselves refer the examination, and to the Intelligence, to discover their real worth, and observe with what care and judgement they have been collected; among these are entire volumes of Sebastiano and Marco Ricci, and Antonio Canal; and the rest in general of noted Masters, and the same may be said with respect to the originality and Excellency of the others which are in eight frames with Cristal Glasses before them.

Then for the Gemms, their quality and worth will be discover'd from their Engr'en in Copper Plates, one hundred in number and their Illustrations in the printed work before mention'd; which work, my design was to begg His Royal Highness, the Prince of Wales, now the most gracious Sovreign to permit might be ushered into the world under his Royal Patronage; and I most ardently wish this Scheme could be still pursued and perfected; and I recommend, that prior to all others, an offer be humbly made to His Majesty that they might be honoured to be in his Cabinet; so likewise if His Majesty should signify his Pleasure to have the drawings also, Books, etc., this would be the utmost bound of my ambition, that this whole Collection, the work of 40 years uniting together, should be so honourably and advantagiously placed.

As for my Pictures, they are distinctly detail'd in the Catalogue among my Papers, which particularly describes the authors their subjects and measures; under this article are comprehended the celebrated Cartons of Carlo Cignani, which he designed for the work executed and now perishing at Parma, and seven Peices of Sacred Story, the most copious and labour'd work of Sebastiano Ricci; both these, which were the Furniture of Two Rooms, are excellently well engraven on Copper Plates, by John Michel Liotard, of Geneva, for which I paid him One Thousand Pounds sterling, and both these works are elegantly described by Abbate Girardi of Modena, and printed by Pasquali in a Quarto Volume. This is all I think needful to observe concerning these collections, intended to serve as a sort of guide for the Instruction of my Relict and for her greater advantage in disposing of them, and for those who shall assist her therein.

And this I declare to be my last Will and Testament, all written with my own hand, and comprized on six[a] sides of Paper, numbered from No. 1 to No. 6, and sign'd and seal'd in the Presence of the under mentioned Witnesses, in Venice the 5th April 1761.

[a]I say comprised on Seaven sides of Paper (including this last) and numbered No. 1 to 7, sign'd and seal'd in the Presence of the under-written Witnesses, in Venice, the 5th April, 1761.

J. Smith

Seal

Vinct, Warren, A.
G. N. Guyon,
William Murrell.

Codicile—Venice 19 March, 1770

By reason of the frequent absence from Venice of Mr. John Udny, and that it may therefore happen he may not be present at the time it may be thought proper to execute this Will, I therefore Institute in his stead, Mr. Robert Richie, to act in conjunction with Mr. Conraed Martens, and I desire that he will accept of the same present of 100 oz. of wrought silver Plate as a Memorial of his departed Friend.

And whereas the sundry legacys to my Nephew and Nieces of whom the Nephew is since dead, to the survivors (the children of my Sister Margaret Bagwell) and to no others I bequeath the said Legacys, and to such only as shall be living and unmarried at the time of my decease and not otherwise, which Nieces I take to be two and no more. As for the two portraits assigned to be given to Mr. John Udny, these are to appertain to my Widow along with my other Effects.

Thus done in Vence [*sic*] this 19th day of March 1770 and comprized on part of the Eight Side of this Will with my own hand and seal'd in the presence of the three under written witnesses, the day and year above written.

J. Smith

Seal

John Symonds, Witness.
John Watson, Witness.
Alexr. Watson, Witness.

(B) JOSEPH SMITH'S LETTER OF 13 JULY, 1762 [TO JAMES STUART MACKENZIE]

Quoted from the text printed in the Hon. Sir John Fortescue's 'Correspondence of King George the Third', Vol. I (1927), p. 29, No. 23. *See above, p. 11.*

Copy.

Mr. Smith (Late Consul at Venice) His Letter dated 13 July & Rec[d] Aug[st] 14, 1762.

SIR—All I have said relating to My Collection & particularly of its Composing Articles; The Many Years' Labour, some Judgement Employ'd, the charge of forming its union under such fortunate circumstances, now no more to be expected, because the Subjects themselves either are no longer existing or, where similar ones may be, hardly Purcheasable at any Rate; All, I say, that I have mentioned of this kind, proceeded (I thought) from the Nature of the Commands that were enjoyn'd me, and I obey'd them with the greater satisfaction to give thereby a Proof of My Veracity, a Point I have constantly had in View, not to dare to advance any thing, which, on Examination of the Articles themselves should not exactly Correspond with My Description of them.

'Tis from this ingenious Relation and I flatter Myself from Your favourable Opinion of my Probity that You have been pleased to interest Yourself for the Completion of My Wishes, and to have this whole Collection removed to a more permanent & Glorious seat, and by rendering it famous to after Ages, confer on the Collector the greatest Honor He can possibly receive.

When I ask'd Your Protection therein, I then resolv'd to be guided by the Advice of so Generous a Friend without laying you under any Restriction from what I said in my Letter of the 5th May Past, which accompany'd the Sundry Lists, any more than Honestly to mention what you commanded me to do. Viz to Specify whereabouts I esteem'd to be the Real Value; and finding now, by the Honor of Your Letter of the 6th July that upon representing all this to our Royal Master, He has been pleased to think the Collection not to be unworthy of His Possession, My desires are satisfied to their full extent: 'Tis the Royal Possessor that constitutes its Value, and I am free'd from the mortifying Suspicion of being even thought minded to drive a Bargain. In short, it is Your Opinion and Advice that I should offer the whole Collection for Twenty thousand Pounds, half whereof to be paid forthwith and the other half in three years by three Equal Payments with 5 per Cent of interest for what shall remain due:

This then is the Proposal I make, and hereupon You'll be so good to finish the Affair, which as from Your Kind Ingerency has had its Rise, so through Your Continued Favours (as I always intended) it will have its End, by Your consenting, as I desire, in my Name to the above Conditions.

This affair thus concluded, pray permit me to know, by the Honor of a Letter from You, as soon as can be conveniently, that I may with the less Loss of time set about making the Necessary Arrangements in My Affairs in Prosecution of my future Plan of Life; more especially, shall I be attending to receive the proper Instructions how to deliver up all according to the Sundry Lists in Your Hands whether to be to some Person deputed for this Purpose, or if after that so much has been trusted to my Honor and Punctuality, I am to be charged with the sending away of all? How is this to be done? whether by Land or Sea Carriage, and if the Latter, if one of His Majesty's Frigates (as I took the Liberty to Hint) will be order'd to come hither from Leghorn, in which case a Hint of it to the Venetian Ambassadors at Our Court will procure every kind of facility, and if the Expenditure be Committed to My Care, I shall keep & send over an exact Account of Expenses and use the greatest Attention, both in the Safety and Frugality of the Passage.

Had a Consideration of Interest prevailed with Me, I should have insisted that previous to a treaty of Price, the Collection be visited, and trusted to the Event of the most exact Examination, but whatever benefit this might have been attended with, I resign all, and I beg to be permitted to make this most Solemn Declaration, and to be believed, I do it with the same Sincerity, as I hope for happiness, for the rest of My Life, and in a future State, that I am more pleased with the Sum His Majesty thinks fit to give, and I accept it with more willingness, and thankfully than the double from any other Purchaser: For thus, this whole Collection, the Work of my Life, will be preserved entire, and may it not be called in me a Commendable Ambition, that future Ages may know, that this great Collection was made by . . . .? [*sic*] and the greatest and most amiable Prince of the World, His most Gracious Sovereign, did not judge it unworthy of His Regard and Possession?

And now may I beg to be indulged and desire that the £10,000: Sterl. which is to be paid forthwith be remitted to me here by Bills of Exchange payable to my own Name at Usance, which is three Months after Their Date, which can be easily done by giving the Order to any Merchant, this may prove of some Benefit to me without any Loss to the Remitter, who besides (it may be) a trifling Commission will give out no more than the £10,000, and if I shall be further favour'd, and it be convenient to have this done soon, I shall be the better enabled to terminate My Concerns in this City, and be so much the sooner hastening to return Home, when my first care will be to beg to have the Honor to pay My Duty to His Majesty, and personally to confess the Obligations, I lye under to my Noble and Generous Friends, and why may I not Subjoyn, to revisit those other old Acquaintance so fortunately transplanted to a situation more worthy to possess them, and where they'll shine with more Lustre, and enjoy the culture they deserve. I must not conclude without thanking You, My Dear & generous Sir, for this Testimony of Your Esteem'd Friendship, by which You have so essentially Contributed to the Comfort and Happiness of my future Life, which I desire to enjoy no longer than I shall preserve and own a just and grateful sense of Your Favour. I have the Honor &c.

P.S.—I have received the Drawing Mr. Dalton sends me by Your Order, and I shall endeavour it be executed by the best Engraver this Place Affords. I wish Mr. Strange were here, or maybe like to be in time for the Purpose, but 'tis much to be doubted. The Work I am sure merits the greatest Artist of the Age: for the same Reason that none but Dioscorides was permitted to cut the Head of Augustus, or Apelles paint Alexander.

(C) RICHARD DALTON'S RECEIPT, 28 JANUARY, 1763

Quoted from the original MS inscription in a copy of the 'Bibliotheca Smithiana' of 1755 in the British Museum (King's Library; 123.e.10.). It is on pp. LXVI and LXVII of 'Addenda & Corrigenda'. See above, p. 12.

No. 5

I underwritten confess to have receiv'd from Mr. Jos. Smith all the books express'd in the present catalogue and the addenda comprised in a Volume in quarto intitled Bibliotheca Smithiana printed by Pasquali at Venice in the year 1755, all in perfect good order & this by Virtue of an order given to me by the Rt. Honble J. S. Mackenzie by the Command and for the account of His Majesty King George the Third, signifiy'd to the said Smith by the said Mr. Mackenzie in his letters dated the 24 August 1762 (which I have seen) which advises the said Smith of the Contract he had concluded for the said Books (part of his Collection) according to the conditions stipulated and expressd therein in the said letter 24 August 1762, for the whole collection, all which I have receiv'd and upon the most dilligent Examination have found to agree most exactly with the distinct catalogue presented by Mr. Smith. In Witness whereof I have sign'd & seal'd double receipts of this Tenor and date.

Venice January 28 1763
Richd. Dalton.
Seal.

[On p. LXXXVIII of the *Bibliotheca Smithiana*, 1755, covered by the above receipt, the album containing the works of Canaletto is listed as follows: "Canal, Antonius. *Experimenta & Schedae.* fol m. lig. corio deaur."].

(D) THE LIST OF CONTENTS OF CANALETTO'S *EXPERIMENTA ET SCHEDÆ*. *See above p. 11.*

Volume de Dissegni di
Antonio Canale di Foglin° . . . 100
senza il Frontispizio
Contiene Dissegni . . . . . . N° 139
et Più
Stampe da Esso incise n° 21
con altre due incise da
altri in Londra di due
vedute di quella Città, dalle
dipinte pure di Esso, et sono
Le medesime dipinte anche
(per) Giuseppe Smith.
Fra quanti dissegni sono altresì
quelli dè Quadri chè questo valente Professore
dipinse (per) detto Smith et che si ritrovanno nelle
sue Case, in Venezia, et nella Villa di Moggiano
No 3.

PLATES

1. VENICE: THE PIAZZETTA WITH THE TORRE DELL' OROLOGIO (Cat. No. 2)

2. VENICE: PIAZZA DI S. MARCO, FACING THE BASILICA (Cat. No. 5)

3. VENICE: PIAZZA DI S. MARCO, FACING THE CHURCH OF S. GEMINIANO (Cat. No. 6)

4. VENICE: S. MARIA DELLA SALUTE FROM THE PIAZZETTA (Cat. No. 3)

5. VENICE: THE PROCURATIE VECCHIE FROM THE PIAZZETTA (Cat. No. 7)

6. VENICE: THE MOLO WITH T

CINTORO AT ANCHOR (Cat. No. 7)

7. VENICE: THE ZECCA AND ADJACENT BUILDINGS (Cat. No. 9)

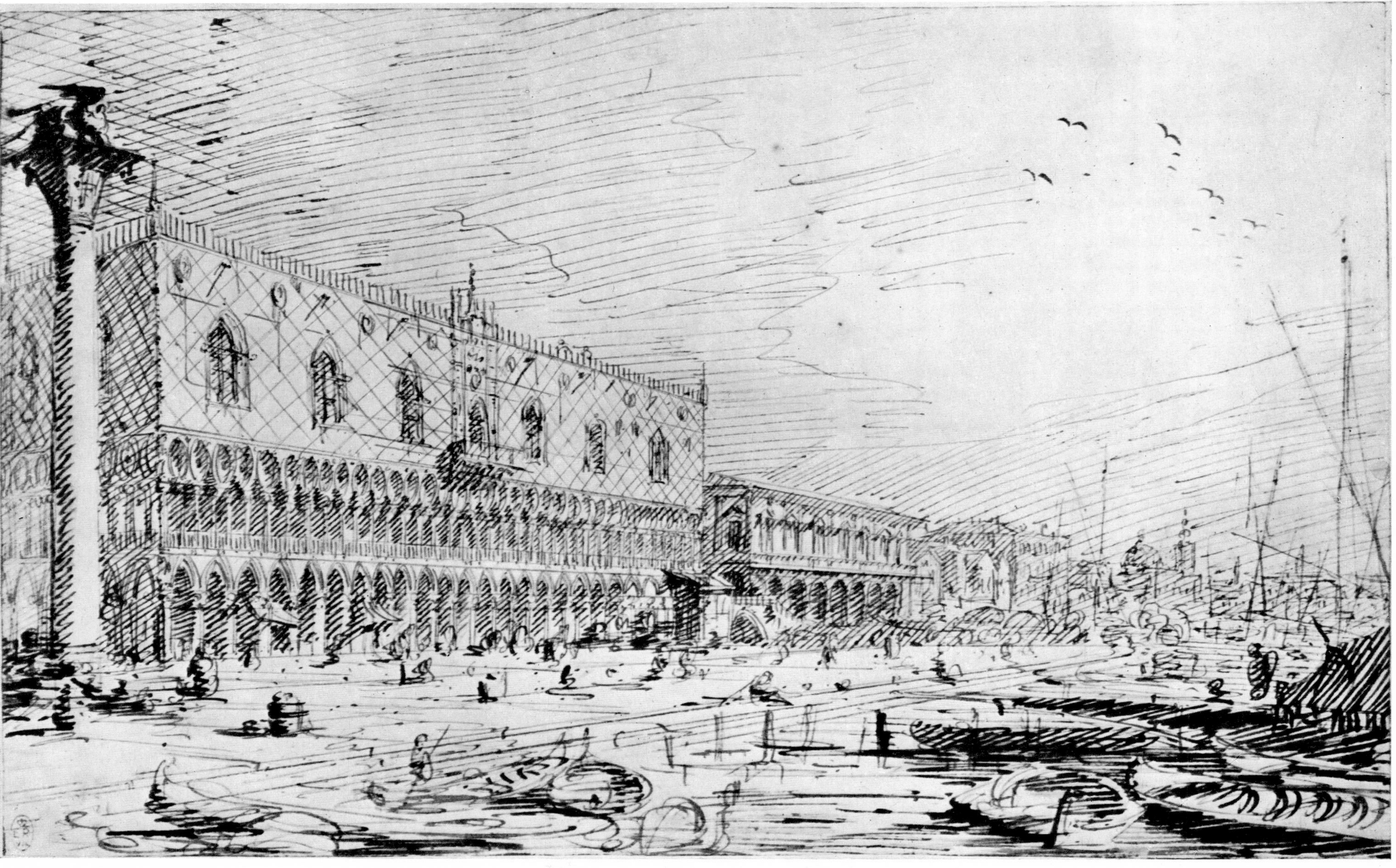

8. VENICE: RIVA DEGLI SCHIAVONI (Cat. No. 10)

9. VENICE: THE PIAZZETTA, FACING S. GIORGIO MAGGIORE (Cat. No. 8)

10. VENICE: CANALE DI S. CHIARA (Cat. No. 13)

11. VENICE: THE TORRE DELL' OROLOGIO AND PIAZZETTA DEI LEONCINI (Cat. No. 27)

12. VENICE: THE LIBRERIA AND CAMPANILE FROM THE PIAZZETTA (Cat No. 25)

13. VENICE: THE PROCURATIE NUOVE FROM THE PIAZZETTA DEI LEONCINI (Cat. No. 42)

14. VENICE: THE FACADE OF S. MARCO AND THE DOGE'S PALACE (Cat. No. 26)

15. VENICE: THE NORTH TRANSEPT OF S. MARCO (Cat. No. 30)

16. VENICE: A SARCOPHAGUS RELIQUARY IN THE NORTH TRANSEPT OF S. MARCO (Cat. No. 31)

17. VENICE: THE LIBRERIA FROM THE MOLO (Cat. No. 43)

18. VENICE: THE LIBRERIA FROM THE MOLO (Cat. No. 44)

19. VENICE: THE DOGE'S PALACE FROM THE CANALE DI S. MARCO (Cat. No. 46)

20. VENICE: THE DOGE'S PALACE FROM THE CANALE DI S. MARCO (Cat. No. 47)

21. VENICE: IL REDENTORE (Cat. No. 54)

22. VENICE: S. MARIA DELLA SALUTE WITH THE DOGANA BEYOND (Cat. No. 53)

23. VENICE: THE ANGLE OF THE DOGE'S PALACE WITH S. GIORGIO MAGGIORE BEYOND (Cat. No. 12)

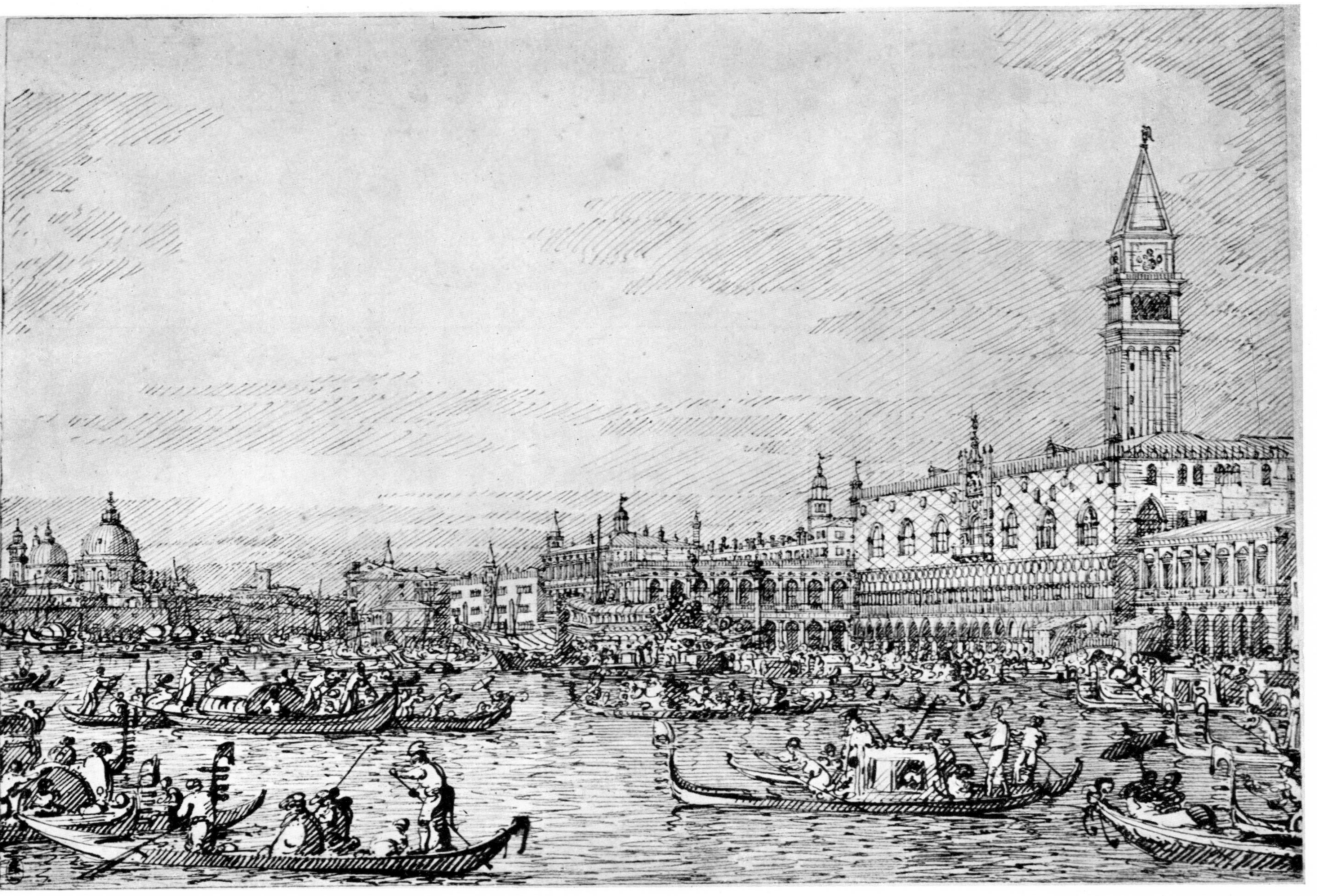

24. VENICE: THE CANALE DI S. MARCO WITH THE BUCINTORO AT ANCHOR (Cat. No. 22)

25. VENICE: THE UPPER REACHES OF THE GRAND CANAL, FACING S. CROCE (Cat. No. 16)

26. VENICE: THE LOWER REACHES OF THE GRAND CANAL FROM NEAR PALAZZO CORNER (Cat. No. 17)

27. VENICE: THE LOWER REACHES OF THE GRAND CANAL FROM NEAR PALAZZO CORNER (Cat. No. 18)

28. VENICE: THE LOWER REACHES OF THE GRAND CANAL, FACING THE BEND (Cat. No. 19)

29. VENICE: THE BEND IN THE LOWER REACHES OF THE GRAND CANAL (Cat. No. 20)

30. VENICE: THE LOWER MIDDLE REACHES OF THE GRAND CANAL, FACING THE RIALTO (Cat. No. 21)

31. VENICE: THE ARSENAL AND PONTE DEL PARADISO (Cat. No. 29)

32. VENICE: VIEW ALONG THE RIVA DEGLI SCHIAVONI, FACING TOWARDS S. MARCO (Cat. No. 23)

33. VENICE: VIEW ACROSS THE BACINO FROM THE RIVA DEGLI SCHIAVONI (Cat. No. 24)

34. VENICE: THE FONTEGHETTO DELLA FARINA FROM THE MOLO DI TERRA-NOVA (Cat. No. 48)

35. VENICE: THE FONTEGHETTO DELLA FARINA FROM THE MOLO DI TERRA-NOVA (Cat. No. 49)

36. VENETIAN CAPRICCIO: THE FONTEGHETTO DELLA FARINA IN FANCIFUL SETTING (Cat. No. 51)

37. VENICE: S. MARCO SEEN FROM THE ARCADE OF THE PROCURATIE NUOVE (Cat. No. 57)

38. VENICE: VIEW IN THE SESTIERE OF DORSODURO (Cat. No. 65)

39. VENICE: VIEW OF THE CITY FROM THE PUNTA DI S. ANTONIO (Cat. No. 66)

40. ISOLA DI S. ELENA AND THE LAGOON (Cat. No. 67)

41. ISOLA DI S. ELENA AND THE DISTANT COASTLINE OF THE LIDO (Cat. No. 68)

42. AN ISLAND IN THE LAGOON (Cat. No. 70)

43. MURANO: THE CHURCH OF S. GIOVANNI BATTISTA (Cat. No. 69)

44. THE PAVILION OF A VILLA ON THE VENETIAN TERRAFERMA (Cat. No. 97)

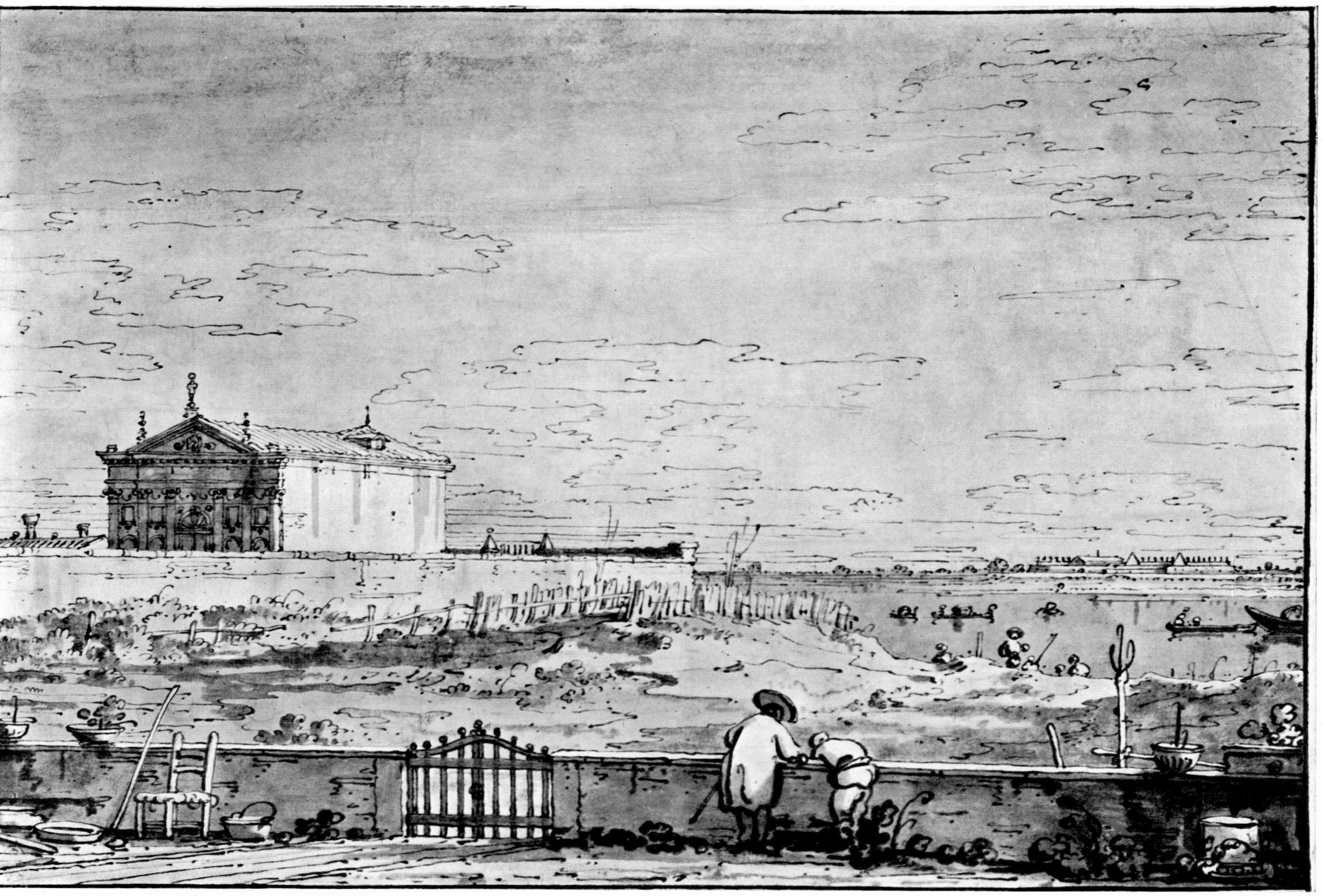

45. THE PAVILION OF A VILLA ON THE VENETIAN TERRAFERMA (Cat. No. 98)

46. VEDUTA IDEATA WITH REMINISCENCES OF CHIOGGIA (Cat. No. 120)

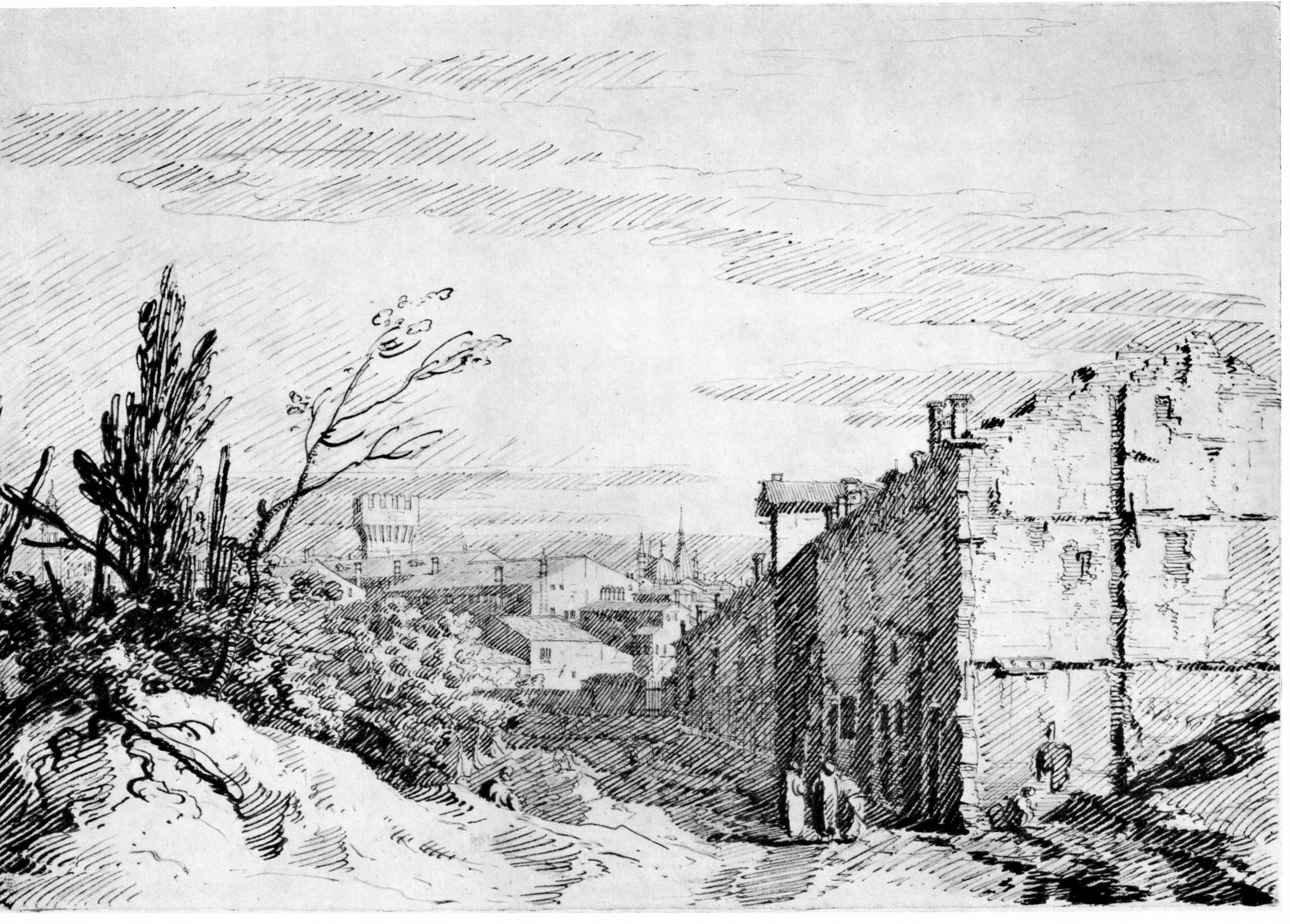

47. PADUA: VIEW OF THE OUTSKIRTS WITH THE TORRE DI EZZELINO AND S. ANTONIO (Cat. No. 81)

48. PADUA: DISTANT VIEW OF S. ANTONIO FROM THE RAMPARTS (Cat. No. 74)

49. PADUA: DISTANT VIEW OF S. GIUSTINA AND S. ANTONIO FROM THE RAMPARTS (Cat. No. 75)

50. PADUA: A VILLA ON THE C

KIRTS OF THE CITY (Cat. No. 84)

51. PADUA: OUTSKIRTS OF THE CITY (Cat. No. 78)

52. PADUA: PALAZZO DELLA RAGIONE (Cat. No. 83)

53. PADUA: THE PRATO DELLA VALLE (L. HALF) WITH S. GIUSTINA (Cat. No. 72)

54. PADUA: THE PRATO DELLA VALLE (R. HALF) WITH THE CHURCH OF THE MISERICORDIA (Cat. No. 73)

55. PADUA: S. GIUSTINA FROM THE RAMPARTS (Cat. No. 76)

56. PADUA: THE PORTELLO AND BRENTA CANAL (Cat. No. 82)

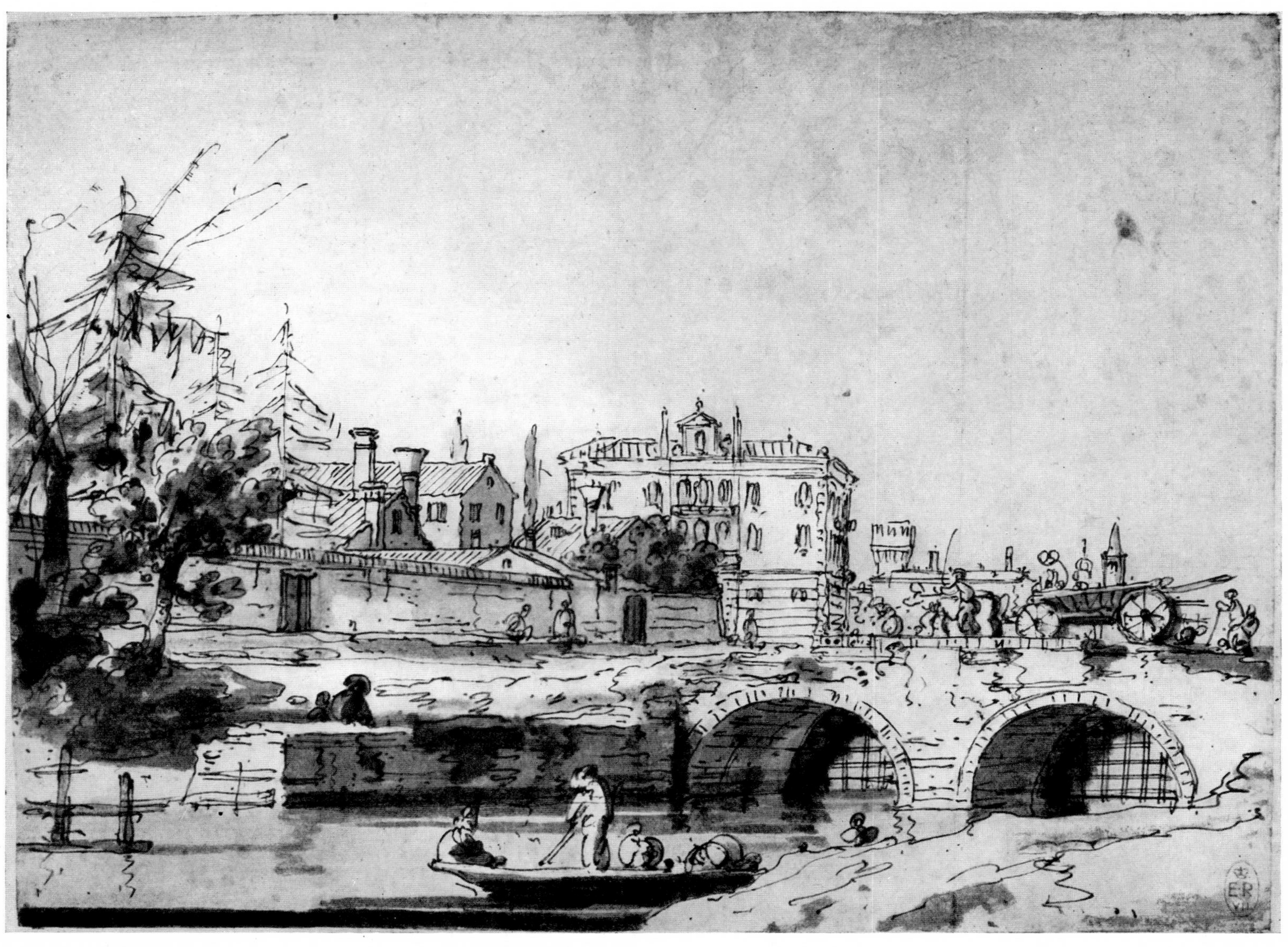

57. PADUA: THE RIVIERA DI S BENEDETTO (?) (Cat. No. 85)

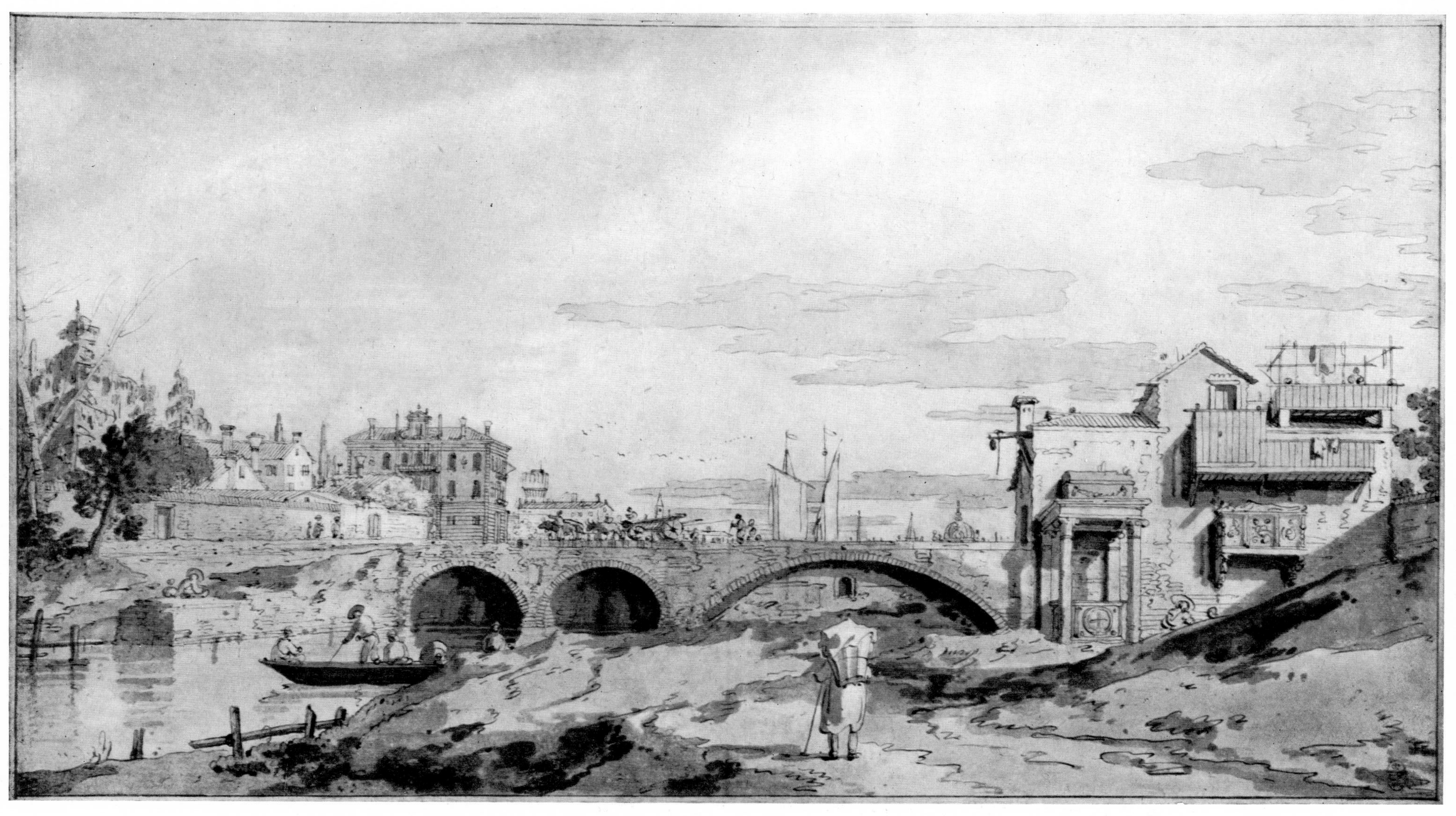

58. PADUAN CAPRICCIO: THE RIVIERA DI S. BENEDETTO (?) IN FANCIFUL SETTING (Cat. No. 86)

59. BRIDGE OVER A RIVER (THE BRENTA OR BACCHIGLIONE?) (Cat. No. 87)

60. BRIDGE OVER A RIVER (THE BRENTA OR BACCHIGLIONE ?) (Cat. No. 88)

61. MESTRE: THE EXTREMITY OF THE CANALE DELLE BARCHE (Cat. No. 89)

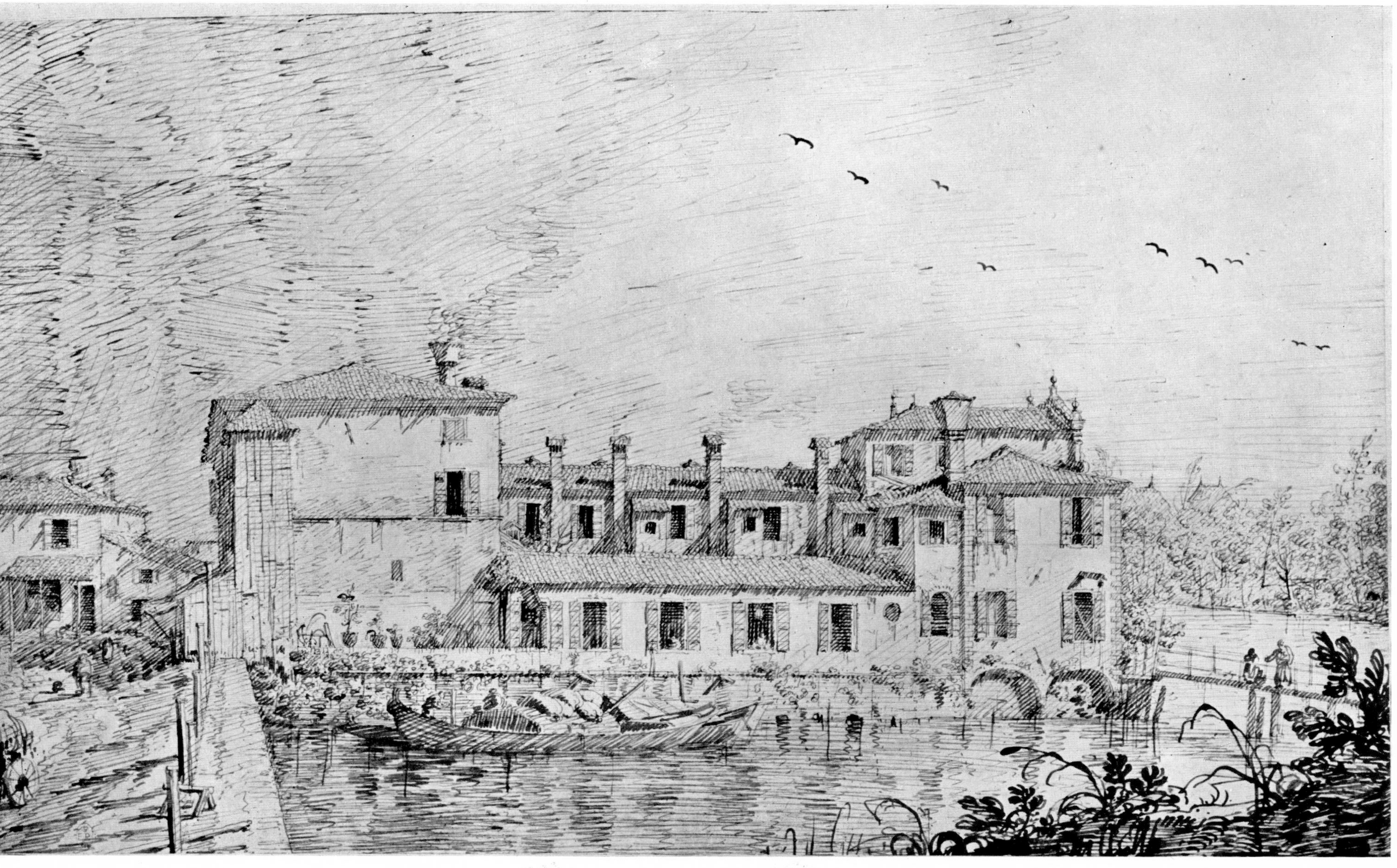

62. A COUNTRY HOUSE ON THE VENETIAN TERRAFERMA (Cat. No. 90)

63. PALAZZO TRON AT DOLO (Cat. No. 92)

64. ROME: DISTANT VIEW OF S. MARIA IN COSMEDIN AND PONTE ROTTO (Cat. No. 102)

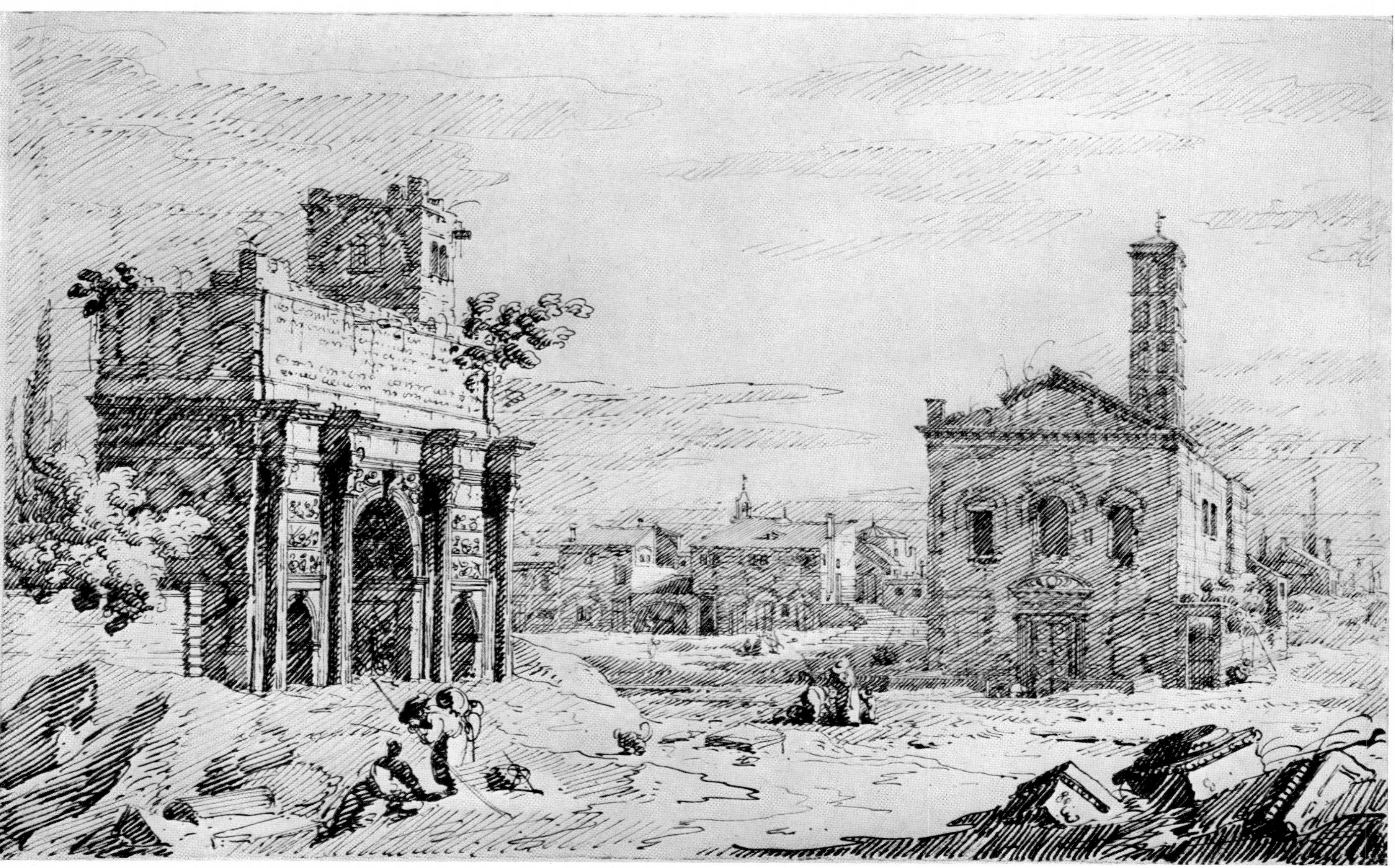

65. ROME: THE ARCH OF SEPTIMUS SEVERUS WITH S. ADRIANO (Cat. No. 103)

66. ROME: THE TEMPLE OF ANTONINUS AND FAUSTINA (Cat. No. 104)

67. ROMAN CAPRICCIO: THE TEMPLE OF VESPASIAN IN FANCIFUL SETTING (Cat. No. 107)

68. ROMAN CAPRICCIO: THE TEMPLE OF SATURN IN FANCIFUL SETTING (Cat. No. 106)

69. LONDON: VIEW OF THE CITY FROM THE TERRACE OF SOMERSET HOUSE (Cat. No. 114)

70. DETAIL OF PLATE 69

71. LONDON: VIEW OF WESTMINSTER FROM THE TERRACE OF SOMERSET HOUSE (Cat. No. 115)

72. DETAIL OF PLATE 71

73. LONDON: WESTMINSTER BRIDGE WITH DISTANT VIEW OF LAMBETH PALACE (Cat. No. 116)

74. DETAIL OF PLATE 73

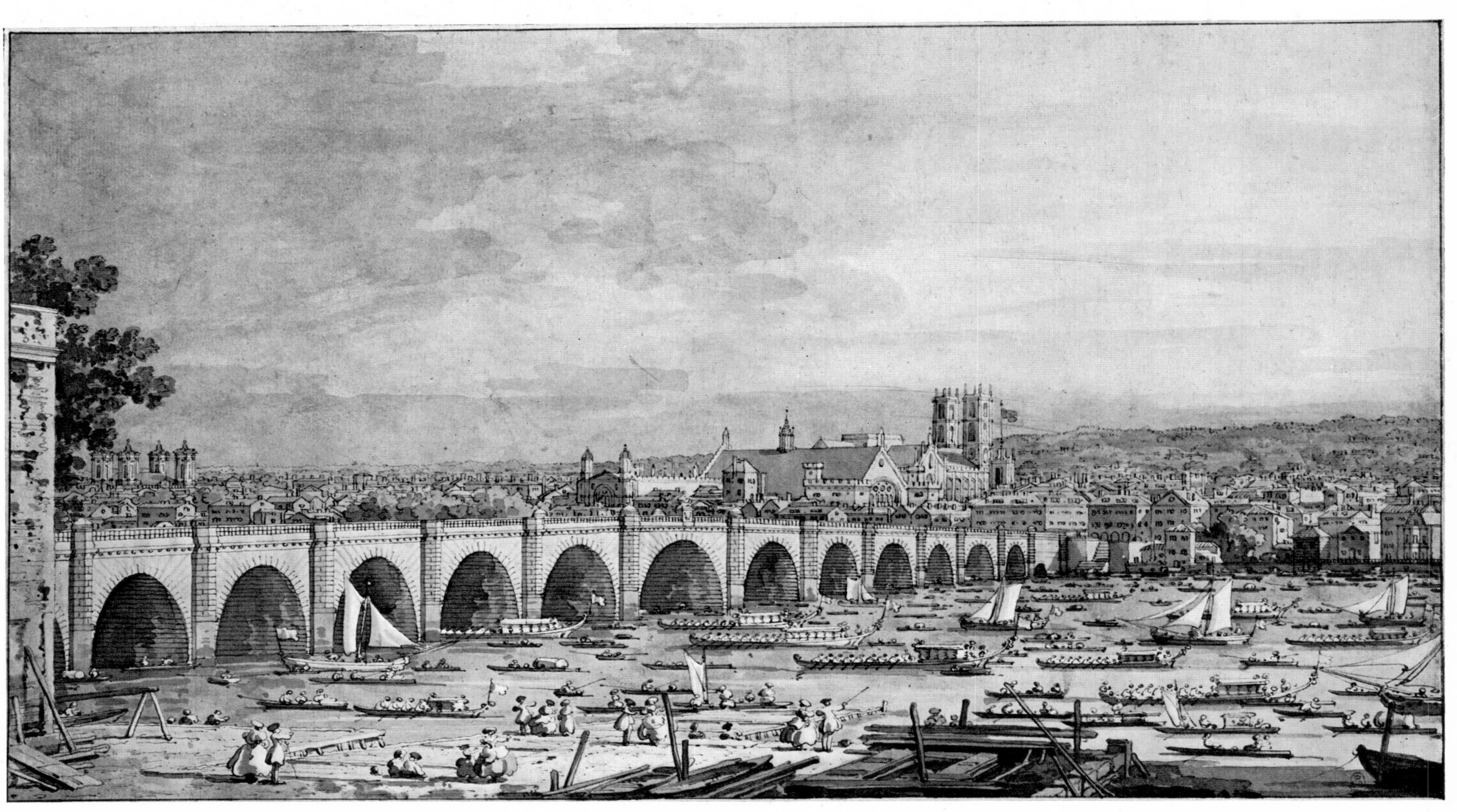

75. LONDON: WESTMINSTER BRIDGE WITH A PROCESSION OF CIVIC BARGES (Cat. No. 117)

76. LONDON: WESTMINSTER BRIDGE UNDER CONSTRUCTION (Cat. No. 118)

77. LONDON: ST. PAUL'S SEEN THROUGH AN

RCH OF WESTMINSTER BRIDGE (Cat. No. 119)

78. VEDUTA IDEATA: RUINS ON A SHORE WITH MOUNTAINOUS COASTLINE (Cat. No. 132)

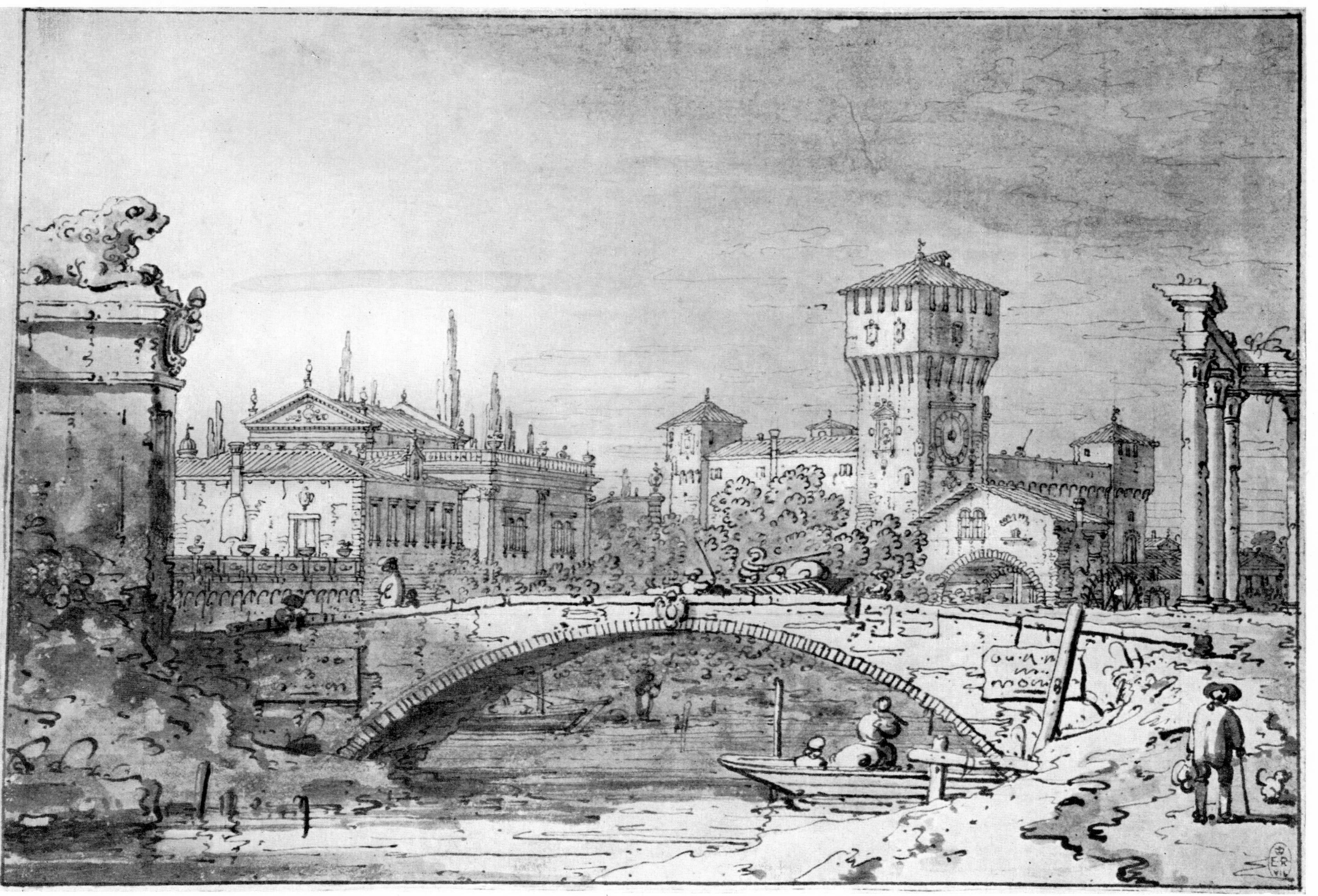

79. VEDUTA IDEATA WITH REMINISCENCES OF PADUA AND VICENZA (Cat. No. 124)

80. VEDUTA IDEATA: A FOUNTAIN ON THE SHORES OF A LAGOON (Cat. No. 130)

81. VEDUTA IDEATA: A MEDIEVAL TOMB AMID CLASSICAL RUINS (Cat. No. 131)

82. VEDUTA IDEATA: A CLASSICAL ARCHWAY ON THE SHORES OF A LAGOON (Cat. No. 133)

83. ROMAN CAPRICCIO: THE ARCH OF TITUS IN FANCIFUL SETTING (Cat. No. 113)

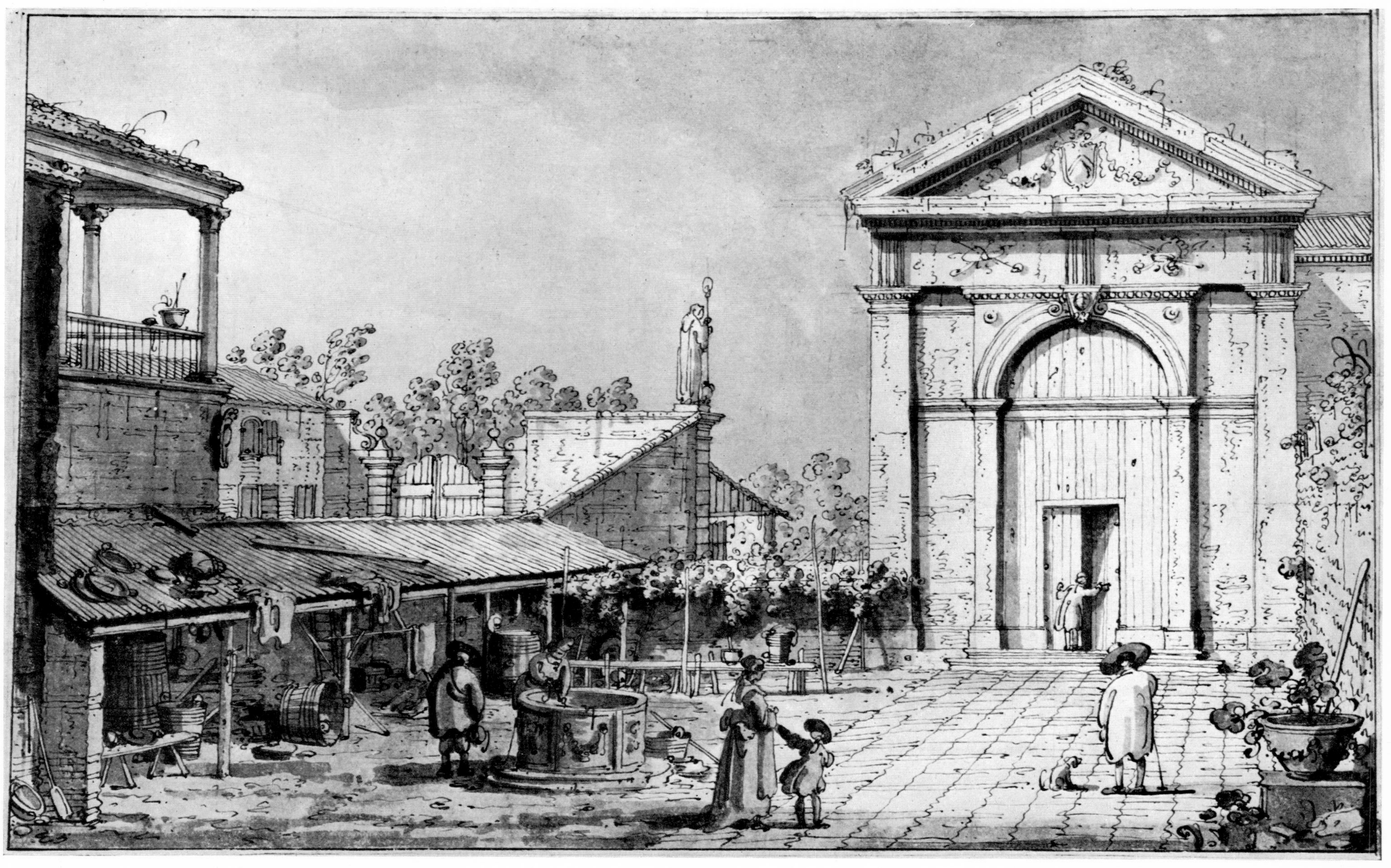

84. VEDUTA IDEATA: THE PAVILION AND COURTYARD OF A VILLA (Cat. No. 140)

85. VEDUTA IDEATA: A HOUSE AND FOUNTAIN ADJOINING A RUINED ARCH (Cat. No. 136)

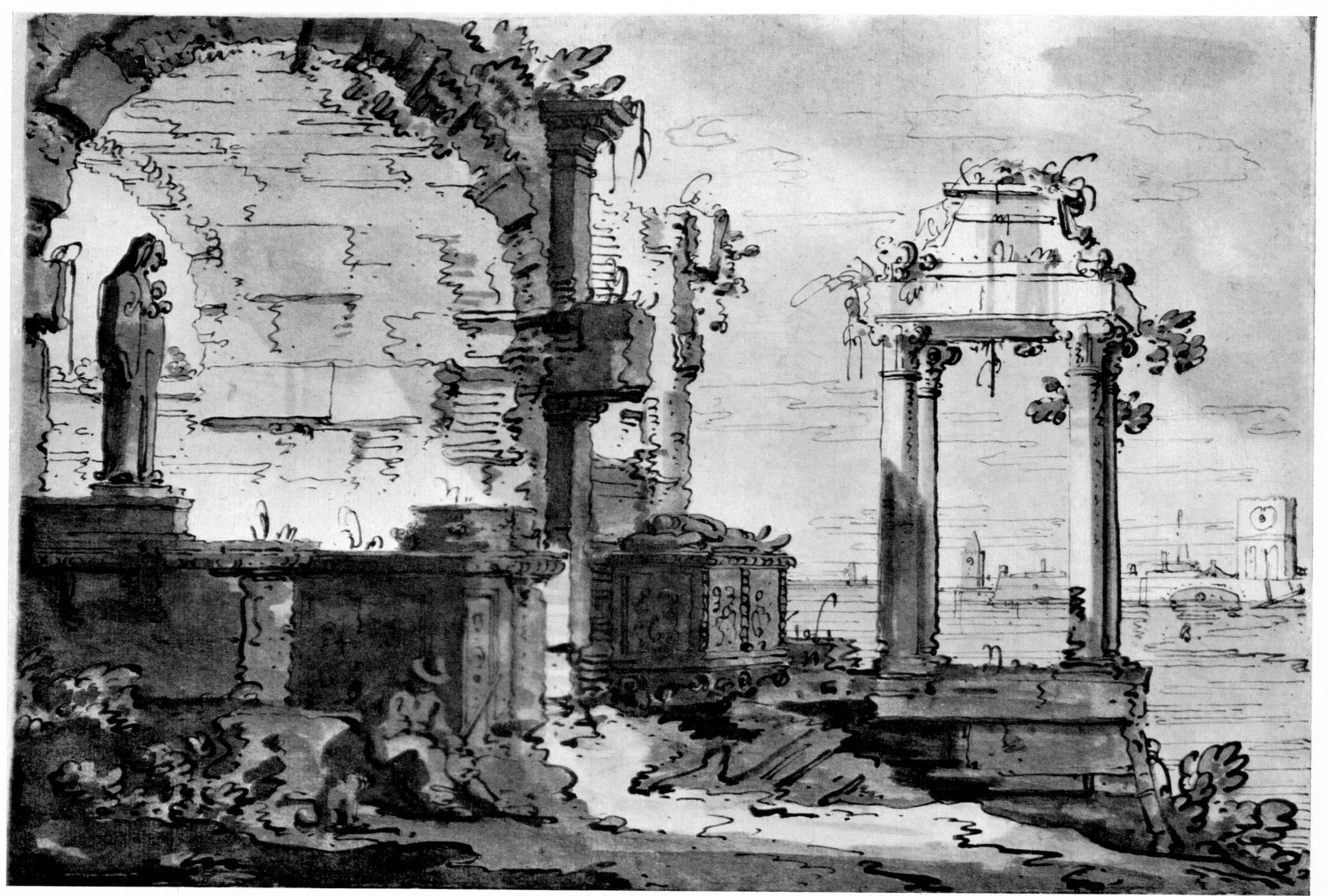

86. VEDUTA IDEATA: RUINS OF A CHURCH ON THE SHORES OF A LAGOON (Cat. No. 134)

87. VEDUTA IDEATA WITH REMINISCENCES OF PADUA (Cat. No. 123)

88. ARCHITECTURAL FANTASY: A FLIGHT OF STEP

LEADING TO THE LOGGIA OF A PALACE (Cat. No. 141)

89. ARCHITECTURAL FANTASY: A CLASSICAL GATEWAY IN A GARDEN (Cat. No. 142)

TABLE OF REFERENCES
AND
MAP OF THE GRAND CANAL

TABLE OF REFERENCES

WINDSOR	PARKER			HADELN			WINDSOR	PARKER			HADELN		
Inventory No.	*Cat. No.*	*Plate*	*Fig.*	*Page*	*No.*	*Plate*	*Inventory No.*	*Cat. No.*	*Plate*	*Fig.*	*Page*	*No.*	*Plate*
7422	62		31	17	7422		7494	36		17	24	7494	
3	42	13		17	3		5	71		34	24	5	
4	61		30	17	4		6	91		38	24	6	33
5	27	11		17	5	29	7	88	60		24	7	22
6	55	*Frontp.*		18	6	42	8	87	59		24	8	
7	57	37		18	7		9	76	55		24	9	
8	26	14		18	8		7500	77		35	24	7500	
9	5	2		18	9	4	1	79		36	24	1	
7430	30	15		18	7430	30	2	80		37	24	2	
1	31	16		18	1	31	3	83	52		24	3	
2	28		12	18	2		4	82	56		25	4	21
3	56		26	18	3		5	75	49		25	5	
4	6	3		18	4		6	74	48		25	6	23
5	59		28	18	5		7	81	47		25	7	
6	58		27	19	6		8	123	87		25	8	36
7	25	12		19	7		9	72	53		25	9	
8	60		29	19	8		7510	73	54		25	7510	
9	43	17		19	9		1	85	57		25	1	
7440	44	18		19	7440		2	96		42	25	2	
1	8	9		19	1	5	3	86	58		25	3	
2	12	23		19	2		4	84	50		26	4	
3	2	1		19	3	3	5	97	44		26	5	
4	1	5		19	4	2	6	102	64		26	6	19
5	3	4		19	5	1	7	109		48	26	7	
6	4		8	19	6		8	110		49	26	8	
7	63		32	20	7		9	112		51	26	9	
8	45		23	20	8		7520	106	68		26	7520	
9	47	20		20	9		1	107	67		26	1	
7450	46	19		20	7450		2	104	66		26	2	25
1	7	6		20	1	6	3	113	83		26	3	
2	10	8		20	2		4	108		47	27	4	
3	22	24		20	3		5	105		46	27	5	
4	24	33		20	4		6	131	81		27	6	
5	23	32		20	5	16	7	129		58	27	7528	
6	66	39		20	6	34	8	134	86		27	7529	
7	11		9	20	7	9	9	128		57	27	7530	
8	69	43		21	8		7530	136	85		27	7531	
9	52		25	21	9		1	111		50	27	7532	
7460	9	7		21	7460	8	2	125		54	27	7533	
1	53	22		21	1		3	133	82		27	7534	
2	50		24	21	2	27	4	132	78		27	7535	
3	51	36		21	3	38	5	127		56	28	7536	
4	48	34		21	4		6	126		55	28	7537	
5	49	35		21	5		7	130	80		28	7538	26
6	64		33	21	6		8	103	65		28	7527	
7	32		13	21	7		9	143		63	28	7539	
8	20	29		21	8		7540	120	46		28	7540	
9	17	26		21	9		1	124	79		28	1	
7470	18	27		22	7470		2	78	51		28	2	
1	21	30		22	1		3	98	45		28	3	
2	16	25		22	2		4	140	84		28	4	
3	14		10	22	3		5	139		62	28	5	
4	19	28		22	4		6	138		61	28	6	
5	37		18	22	5	20	7	137		60	29	7	
6	13	10		22	6	11	8	135		59	29	8	
7	29	31		22	7	28	9	90	62		29	9	
8	38		19	22	8	17	7550	95		41	29	7550	
9	39		20	22	9		1	92	63		29	1	
7480	41		22	22	7480	18	2	94		40	29	2	
1	40		21	23	1		3	93		39	29	3	
2	35		16	23	2		4	99		43	29	4	
3	54	21		23	3		5	101		45	29	5	12
4	34		15	23	4		6	100		44	29	6	
5	33		14	23	5		7	117	75		29	7	
6	65	38		23	6		8	116	73		30	8	
7	68	41		23	7		9	115	71		30	9	47
8	67	40		23	8		7560	114	69		30	7560	
9	15		11	23	9	10	1	119	77		30	1	45
7490	89	61		23	7490	15	2	118	76		30	2	
1	70	42		23	1	32	3	142	89				
2	121		52	24	2		4	141	88				
3	122		53	24	3								

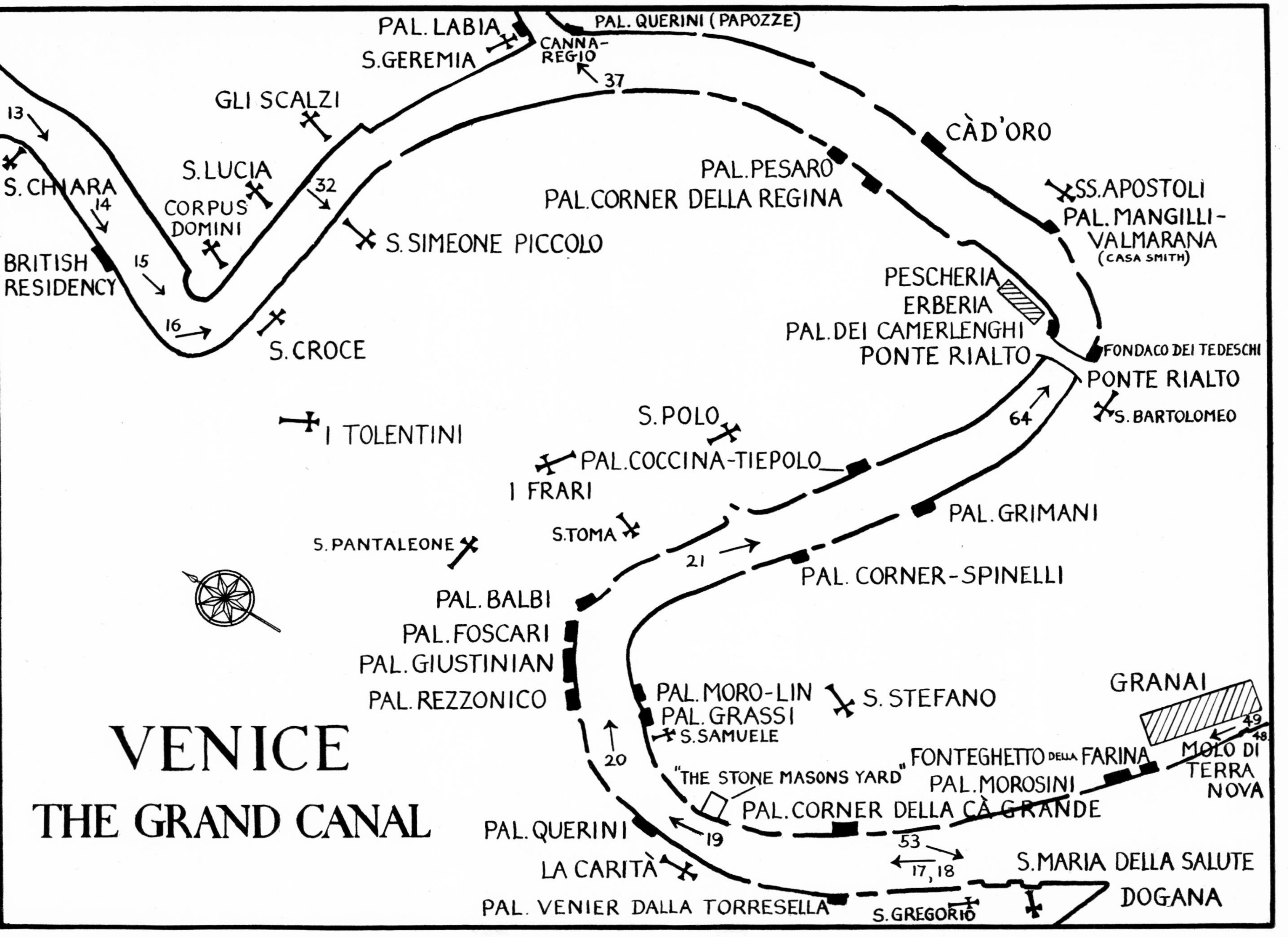

MAP OF THE GRAND CANAL ON WHICH ARE PLOTTED THE VIEWPOINTS OF CANALETTO'S DRAWINGS

(THE NUMBERS REFER TO THE CATALOGUE, <u>NOT</u> TO THE PLATES)

The reproductions in this Volume are from a new set of photographs taken by Alfred Carlebach, F.R.P.S.